CHICAGO
STREET CORNER
STORIES

by

Roger Wright

Chicago Street Corner Stories
by Roger Wright
Think Different Press

Published by Think Different Press
  Chicago, Illinois USA
Copyright ©2021 Roger Wright

Cover and interior illustrations:
  Diana Ani Stokely at GRAFIX *to go*

Library of Congress Control Number: 2013931055
ISBN: 978-0-988043-2-3 paperback
ISBN: 978-0-9889043-3-0 ebook

Dedicated to all the street corner stories yet to be told.

Table of Contents

Greetings

We all have our stories. They can tell us who we are. Why we care. How to make sense of our world. And that's just a start. Stories can capture those golden moments of a lifetime when everything changes, they can build legacies, and can hold fast to that most delightfully delicious question, "*What if?*" A question that hovers over every story in this collection.

Three kinds of stories may be found here. In **PART 1: Ghosts Talk,** discover the lady detective whose spirit walks with Abraham Lincoln. Find Charles Dickens's brother buried in Chicago. Look one way to see Mike Royko still fighting a bully. Look the other way to see Hemingway haunting a corporation. Ready for some music? The spirit of Bob Gibson, the man who some say invented folk music, is still strumming his 12-string in spirit. And the prize fighter, Jack Johnson, is still jabbing and punching for respect.

When ghost's talk, the story might be about something that just took a moment. But the message could settle in and last us a lifetime.

1

The story of the girl with the empty eyes haunts me still:

> On a brilliant summer day in Chicago, walking north along the grand, busy, boulevard Michigan Avenue, six young teenagers from the inpatient psychiatric unit cluster around me, their counselor. It's my first job out of school and this walk, under my supervision, is the off-ward activity for the day.
>
> We're all walking, laughing, enjoying the sunshine. Mary, one of my charges, suddenly darts from our group, and steps off the curb into the path of an oncoming car. Before she could follow with her other foot into the street, I reach out, my hand locking like a vise on her upper arm and I yank her back to safety on the sidewalk.
>
> "Mary," I say, looking hard into her empty eyes that haunt me down through the years, "when a moving car hits you, it hurts." Mary smiles. Her eyes, though, are brutal, cold, and absent of any shred of humanity. And she says, "Oh I've been hit by a car before. It doesn't hurt at all."

Those empty eyes from decades ago stare straight down at me this very moment, scorching a message in my heart, that bona fide crazy exists in the world. Can we remember to take care, to reach out, and to do everything we can to pull another from their pain?

PART 2: What Love Did, starts off at the street corner of Michigan and Huron. Walking south, traveling back in time again, over the river, to see a young couple cross the street with their heads down against the winter wind:

> *Taking her hand out of the pocket of her red winter coat, she links her arm with his. Beaming a smile so bright that no words do it justice, she looks up at him and says something out of hearing. They both laugh.*

That moment, the one where they link arms, that's the kind of moment to be found in PART 2. Hear the clarion call. Find the love in life. Find it in the most unusual places. In these stories about *what love did*, find out what happens when a movie star steps off the screen and starts munching on your popcorn. Watch love unfold between a child and his parents. And share with me a love story on a Chicago rooftop under cheering stars.

In **PART 3: Hope Remains**, we begin on the corner of Michigan and Erie. Looking east into the sprawling medical campus, someone is saying, "It's a chronic disease. No cure, but drugs can help you blanket the symptoms." This is the time when we, and the recipient of this news, begin the search for stories of hope. Like the one about a message to a young inventor. Like the story of the train derailment, when baby Annie Beth survived, though everyone around her died. And the one where hope is found during a chance Thanksgiving street corner meeting.

We close this collection with stories of hope — because hope remains.

So. Let's get back to those ghosts. Because they have some stories. And ghosts do talk.

PART 1: Ghosts Talk

ROGER WRIGHT

Introduction: Walking West from Graceland

What Ghosts? And why are they talking?

Walking just west of Graceland Cemetery in Chicago, around the corner from the blazing neon beacon of the Diner Grill, there is a backyard tent that looks like it could have been Ulysses S. Grant's battlefield headquarters. Or maybe someplace Hemingway would stay on a hunting trip to the green fields of Africa. Through the screens of this tent, a scene emerges from another time. An ancient quilt on a musty bed. A nightstand with a photograph of a wide-eyed woman who looks like she never sleeps. Next to her picture, a glass half full of water begs the question, "Is she coming back to finish that water?" On the pillow is a book, a Dickens classic propped open to the title page with a handwritten inscription reading, "From your brother, Charles." A dusty pair of boxing gloves hang across a coat rack in the corner.

Who lives here? And why does walking past this backyard bedroom make the heart beat just a little faster?

Then, *"Why are all the tent flaps thrown open?"*

Perhaps a nod to Abraham welcoming faithful travelers from every direction, or perhaps whoever lives there just likes to sleep in the open air.

But it gets cold here. And this is a big city. With lots of big city problems, where walls come in pretty handy.

Among the living, there are those who can beat back walls. But ghosts have no use for walls.

Could this tent be the place where the ghosts meet the living? Could this tent be where ghost's talk?

Within the tent, faint echoes of music blend with laughter, the sounds billowing out on ancient breezes. Silhouettes of people emerge. Formed from swirling mist, the outlines of guitars and the crush of a party takes shape.

The music becomes recognizable, the songs almost nameable, the musicians so familiar. It doesn't matter if you know the tune, the song title, or the artist's name, because in this tent, where ghosts mingle with the living, everyone's song can be heard. You hear Muddy Waters growl and Steve Goodman sing a love song. Then Prine gets up to sing about angels. Bonnie Koloc answers with what she believes. Finally, Curtis Mayfield strolls through the city, night stars swirling, with a message of hope. And this is just a start to the party.

Through the open tent flap, folk singer and story teller, Bob Gibson, steps outside. With a big old 12-

string guitar around his neck, he smiles and slaps up a sign that says, WELCOME ALL!

Still smiling, Gibson motions inside, turns and strikes a chord on his 12-string, singing out, "Listen!"

Because sometimes street corner stories can come true.

Augustus Dickens

Graceland Cemetery in Chicago is the final resting place of a collection of both known and unknown souls from the worlds of commerce, the arts, sports, and government. Whether from autumn breezes, or by inspiration from Edgar Lee Master's classic book *Spoon River Anthology*, the ghost moons of October allow the spirits of Graceland Cemetery to be heard.

Under the starbright moons of October I return, because there is so much more to my story. You know my brother. Charles. He wrote books. You do not know me.

I was thirty-nine-years old and reportedly penniless when they laid me in this October soil. The year was 1866. My brother Charles was flush with uncounted millions, but my legacy was my plans ... no one knew that I had plans.

When the autumn leaves come blowing, swirling in a misty woodsmoke haze and dancing in muted golden crinkly brown, orange, and blazing red; my brother Charles rises up from an untold distance to meet me here. Lit by the moon, we walk these grounds of Graceland Cemetery in Chicago. We walk and I recall my plans.

You'll forgive my manners, an introduction is in order. My name is Augustus Dickens. My brother was Charles Dickens. He was fifteen years my senior. He wrote books; told stories that were heard by the world. Heard by the whole world. Read forever. That was my brother. That was not I.

In our lifetimes my brother never came here to Chicago. Certainly not to this quiet island; Graceland Cemetery with its tall red brick walls keeping out the rush and roar of the city. Here where I rest, where passing trains rumble like a distant heartbeat, my neighbors' marble-sculpted markers bestow their elegant morning greetings. Quiet green lawns accompany trees which sway in rhythm to better display their October finery. I am always so proud to welcome my brother here to my final resting place.

I was not always so proud.

I left our native Portsmouth, by the crashing sea, to come to America with my love, Bertha. Yes, there was the matter of my wife Harriett, she who became blind, and was abandoned by me. I was not proud of that. I offer no excuses, but you see, I had plans. There are stories you don't know. Stories even my brother Charles doesn't know or hasn't told.

Can anyone ever really know the stories of another?

Bertha and I went first to Amboy, Illinois. If you draw a straight-line west from where the muddy swamps of commerce called Chicago rests next to a giant lake, you'll find tiny Amboy. From the blinding white prairie snowstorms of February to the muggy long evenings of August, I was the Editor of The Amboy Times. My plans for that newspaper recognized Amboy's promise to come.

I had plans for my store, the People's Cheap Store. Ah, perhaps something in the Green River bubbled up thoughts of new kinds of stores. Samuel Carson was also from Amboy. Carson and Pirie and Scott also had visions of new types of stores. But they didn't have my plans.

I sold the store and bought the small farm. But those prairie winters were hard. In June of 1860, the job with The Illinois Central Land Department opened up. Bertha and I had to go live in Chicago. In those days, the Illinois Central Railroad fueled the prairie like blood reviving a dying man. To be in the middle of all that was just the place for a man with a plan.

In Chicago, we lived at 538 North Clark Street. That was the time of the music. Our home was filled with music; Bertha at the piano, her voice echoing through our rooms like sweet wild fruit, feeding my plans forever and a day.

Yes, I knew the pleasures of the drink. For a man who has plans, a man so far from his home, whose path was uneasy, of course, that man would know the pleasures of the drink. Of course, the drink would help me with my plans.

It wasn't the drink that finally took me, it was the tuberculosis. That is when I came to Graceland, on the outskirts of muddy Chicago. Now it is a full, pulsating city, grown around this quiet island of spirits. This October garden is right in the middle of it all, no longer on the outskirts of anything. This October garden is where, once a year, my brother Charles comes to visit.

After my death, both blind Harriet and my love, Bertha received support from my brother. That is, until that first Christmas Eve after my departure, when Bertha, forlorn, took the morphine, closed her eyes, and joined me.

Sometimes, on a summer evening here in Graceland, I hear faint echoes of Bertha's piano. It brings me comfort to hear her sing while I continue to make my plans.

Now in October, grand and glorious October, when brother Charles joins me here, we walk the quiet paths of my final resting place in Chicago. As autumn leaves swirl down to lay a path to crunch beneath our spirit feet, I tell my brother my plans. Share the rest of my stories.

He hears me. He nods. And my brother, my brother Charles Dickens, the writer, offers me up an October smile.

I'm Kate

My last name? The gravestone says Warn, with no 'e' at the end. But I've had lots of names. When the tall, thin man dressed in black with the sad, haunted eyes comes to visit, every October, here in Graceland Cemetery in Chicago, he just calls me Kate.

I rest near Mr. Pinkerton, now and forever. It should be that way, for without Mr. Pinkerton, I would never have met the tall sad man. Without Mr. Pinkerton, they never would have said, "Kate Warne, she never sleeps."

After I came here to Graceland, people wrote, "Kate Warne, the first lady detective." I never understood why being first was important. What was important, was that I was good.

I was only twenty-three years old when I first stepped in to Mr. Pinkerton's Detective Office in Chicago. That may seem young, but I hadn't been a little girl in a very long time. My husband had passed. So, it was just me, and I needed a job.

I knew I could find out things about people that no one else could. I knew I could find secrets. So, at ten o'clock in the morning of August 23rd, 1856, Mr. Pinkerton gave me the job. I was a detective.

Wives and girlfriends would tell me the things they would never tell a man. Like Mr. Maroney, in Montgomery Alabama. He embezzled $50,000 from his company, the Adams Express Company. And I got the true story from his wife. The true story and $39,515 back to the company.

Mr. Pinkerton was pleased. He said I was one of the best he'd ever known.

Bank robbers and killers, I found their secrets. I stopped their evil deeds. And when I walk these golden-brown grounds of autumn, I am pleased with my life's work. My years were few. I passed soon after the War Between the States when I was thirty-eight years old, but I am pleased with my life's work.

In October, I remember my best work, because it is in October when the sad eyed man comes back to visit me, the one who had just been elected President.

My work with the President-Elect began with the tips we got out of the secessionist plots in Baltimore. The cry to crack open the Union was echoing across the land in those times. Splitting up what America had become.

But it was what I found out next that threatened to rip open the very fabric of these United States and leave it to bleed and die.

There was a plot to kill the new President. Kill him before he even took office. I pieced together the evildoer's plan.

It was to happen when the President-Elect changed trains in Baltimore, during the one-mile carriage ride between the two train stations. The secessionists would cause a diversion. The President-Elect's guards would respond to the diversion. Then a crowd would swarm the unprotected carriage and kill the soon-to-be President. He would never complete the trip from his home in Springfield, Illinois to the muddy streets of Washington. He would never take office. He would die in Baltimore.

But with Mr. Pinkerton by my side, I was able to make the case for what I had found. I convinced the President-Elect that the danger was real.

After the President-Elect's last speech of the evening in Harrisburg Pennsylvania, we changed the travel schedule for the last leg of the trip into Washington, DC. Mr. Pinkerton had the telegraph lines interrupted so no one would know of the change. And then we dressed the President-Elect in the suit of a traveling common man. We put a soft felt hat on his head and told him to carry a shawl as if he was an invalid. When he got on his new train, I cried out a greeting as if he were a long-lost brother.

And throughout that long dark night, as the train pulled into an empty Baltimore at 3:30 a.m., as opposed to the much earlier hour that had been planned, even then, I sat next to him. Kept him safe.

I got him to the White House alive. Because throughout that night I never slept.

He was inaugurated. Became the President. And he saved the union. He kept alive the great American dream.

Which is why he comes to see me each October. He comes to say thanks.

President Abraham Lincoln. The tall, thin man with the haunted sad eyes. He comes here to Graceland. Offers me his arm. And we walk. Through the orange, red and brown scattered leaves of time. He is known by so many as the centuries pass, this President Abraham Lincoln. And few remember my name.

But he remembers. He comes each October and we walk the grounds of Graceland together.

And when I look up at those sad eyes and see him looking back at me under an October moon, I can actually see those haunted eyes, just for a moment, fill with joy.

That happens here. At Graceland Cemetery in Chicago.

Only in October.

At the Church Swimming Pool

Sure, the church smells like chlorine, but nobody complains. Fact is that it's the fastest growing church in, I don't know, the history of religion? Not sure. I really don't know a whole lot about religion. Never cared for it myself.

What I do care about is numbers. And if a church wants to install its own swimming pool in the basement? And the membership numbers in the church go from 30 to 3,000 in two weeks? That gets my attention. I love to swim.

Of course, it takes me awhile to get in. Turns out, there is a waiting list for the place. And then the screening committee review. But I make it. Hot damn! Jackpot! It is like winning a lottery. I am a member.

Church is on a block in the city where there are a lot of indoor swimming pools. Of course, I didn't know that then. It isn't a gated block. Anybody can walk through. But no one does.

And the church has a special service. 10:55 to 11:00 a.m. every Sunday morning. All the folks who take care of the pools in the big houses get to come. The workers are like family, one big family. Time goes on and some of my best friends are the workers. They are just like us.

The pool is the big draw. Family fun and all. But the five-minute church services help, too. Nobody gets bored. Nobody gets mad. Nobody says that one religion is better than another. In fact, I think we really do something for religion in the world because no one fights about it anymore.

We just swim in our pool.

The best part is our lifeguard. Out of 4,032 applicants for the job from sixteen countries, we narrowed it down to one. Really fast. It is the only way to do it. I mean we probably won't get many more. And we did find the perfect guy.

Why is he perfect? Because everybody likes him. In fact, he is impossible to dislike. It is like he has some kind of likeability gene that melds him into being whoever you want him to be. Nicest guy in the world. Doesn't bog us down with a lot of details on religion. Does what we tell him to do. He just talks about sunshine for two or three minutes each week, we sing a song, and then we all go swimming.

Who could complain? It is perfect.

See? We all know that nothing makes people angrier than religion. Don't EVER mess with a pissed-off atheist or agnostic. They will smother you with a passion for the cause that you really don't even want to hear. And religious extremists? Don't get me started.

So, we got a swimming pool.

And the world's best lifeguard.

Of course, there was that time that that poor kid, the youngest daughter of one of the help, fell in the deep end. And our lifeguard wanted to save her. Tried to save her. He ran as fast as he could. And all those rumors about him not jumping in the water because he couldn't swim, none of them were true. He just didn't get there in time.

And I don't know what all the bitchin' is about. This is church. This is where we all agree. This is where we swim.

The kid made it. She didn't die. One of the workers pulled her out. Not sure what his name was. But he pulled her out. She was fine. Oh, sometimes she wakes up crying. But that will pass. We'll all pray for her. We still do prayers. So, we'll pray for her.

Before you know it?

She'll be back swimming again too.

Hemingway's Cubicle

On this summer day of pure silver simmering heat, Hemingway mists into a vacant cubicle on the 32nd floor of the downtown office building and starts looking for the story.

Very few pay him any mind. Most don't see him at all. And no one speaks to him. Ten thousand cubicles squat like artificial rows of vinyl vegetables over countless air-conditioned floors, while outside, the world swelters. This company on the 32nd floor focuses on technology-driven projects. Delivering solutions. Lots of solutions. And project plans. All in support of a flagship product that makes people work longer hours without ever knowing why.

On the counter in Hemingway's cubicle, the computer keyboard and monitor lie dead. He picks up each one. Shakes them. Turns them upside down. Flicks the foreign plastic with his fingers. Presses a key that lights up the screen with the screaming message SHOW ME YOUR PASSWORD!

But he has no password. And still no story.

Turning away from the brittle plastic, he lays his hands on the typewriter that's been discarded in the corner of the empty cubicle. And Hemingway begins to type out nonsense. Letters and words on a page jumbled together. Like a singer clearing his throat before a song.

No one from the acres of cubicles around him says a word about the click-clack chorus of his Corona. This is a technical floor. These are technical people. They assume the typewriter stroke sounds are a new app being tested. Or they just don't hear.

But from that wall of sound and jumbled nonsense, Hemingway hears four clean, clear words:

"Cry.

Hard.

Laugh.

Easy."

He speaks the words "Cry hard" out loud and an image rises up on his computer screen. A woman sits on the edge of an unmade bed, crying hard, shoulders slumped. In one hand, she holds a banged-up tennis racquet pointed in defeat at the floor. The room is dark with bare walls. This corner of Chicago is miles from the downtown tower. The couple who lives here will do no decorating, because there is no couple anymore, they are going their separate ways. That night, after he leaves, a squirrel gnaws its way into the flimsy-walled house, running loose, scrambling, squirming, and foaming scared. The tennis racquet she holds seems to absorb her sadness, becoming a less-than-efficient weapon as she chases the squirrel through the empty rooms, knocking over lamps, and breaking a window. It feels like hours that she chases that squirrel.

Finally, the squirrel intruder skitters out of the house, using its original hole to escape. She stuffs the hole with old sheets, with a piece of wood, and with any remaining dreams that their love could have worked. Hemingway sees her crying hard. And as he watches, he builds his story. The heavy darkness, the piles of unpacked boxes, the musty smells rising from the basement, and the echoes of silence bouncing off the bare kitchen walls where no one ever stayed long enough for dinner.

Having told the story of crying hard, Hemingway hovers over the downtown tower in search of easy laughter. Again, the story comes to him, floating through the killing summer heat waves into the air-conditioned maze of cubicles on another floor of the tower, where he is drawn to a small conference room. Four people sit around a table, three of them bubbling with that energy that comes with their first jobs after completing school. Their eyes are riveted on the fourth person — that same, once-tearful woman from the house of unpainted walls, her hard cries distant or gone, is bubbling too as she talks about how it feels when people work together. Knowing how to face challenges of working together, understanding why sharing a task matters, and celebrating when a person's work involves doing what they do best. Listening intently, they are caught up in her stories, and join in the laughter that she shares within those stories. The sign on the door says TRAINING, but that's not really what's happening here. This sharing of stories prompts a different way of thinking, encourages questions, and builds dreams. This form of energy, this joy that flows by common conduit, invites the listeners to share in easy laughter.

And with that sound of easy laughter, rain begins to fall outside the downtown tower. Nourishing, cleansing, sparkling rain. The rhythm of the city picks up the pace, daily life sheds its torpor and begins to sing along with the rain, awash in splendor.

Hemingway sits back down in his cubicle and smiles, because he found the story.

Gazing out at the rain-swept city coming to life, Hemingway laughs like the laughing is easy.

Bob Gibson, Folksinger, Story Teller

The cricket-chirping darkness was barely lit by the pale orange ghost moon of October, long past late night.

In an unmarked corner of Chicago's Rosehill Cemetery, a distant noise of a solitary car tumbling down Western Avenue into the darkness sounds like the last thing you'll ever hear. For an instant, breathing stops. But then, three strums of a mighty 12-string guitar sound, pushing back the night. The guitar, speaking some sort of language of its own, makes way for this strong and smiling man's voice

Like his album title says, Bob Gibson is here "for to sing."

Hovering ghostly shoulders bump up against each other as an audience assembles. On this street corner of the cemetery lit by the moon, smiling spirits join spirits. But that's not surprising. It's October again, and Bob Gibson has come to sing. As he tunes up his guitar and gets ready to play, ghost time shifts.

***

Far from the Rosehill moonlight, we hear the ring of hammers, the swish of saws, and the shouts of nails

27

pounded on the site of a construction job. This forest glen beside the Hudson River Forest in upstate New York sings with the sounds of a house being built. We must have slipped back in time, because here is young Bob Gibson working a construction job, helping out a skinny fella not much older than he is. This guy he's working for, something about him is different. Talking music, talking better worlds, just being around this guy, name of Pete Seeger, Gibson is learning something.

Bob Gibson buys a banjo with his earnings. His song continues.

***

Back to the moonlight mists of Rosehill Cemetery, a crowd gathers in what feels like a dark and friendly basement room. Bob sings another song, making the music glide out of the darkness, making the music come alive, and time shifts.

***

In another small dark room, just a couple miles east of Rosehill Cemetery is a club with a different beat, where Bob Gibson performs. Ken Nordine's Offbeat Room offers music for the casual listener. Nordine sometimes takes the stage to perform what he calls 'word jazz.'

From the darkness that connects Rosehill Cemetery to Nordine's Offbeat Room, the wind coming off a ghost moon blows toward another friendly dark passage to a different basement. On the corner of Chicago Avenue and Dearborn Street, a guy named Albert Grossman, tired of his job, is thinking about the Offbeat Room and about smoky night joints of Paris reverberating with the likes of Jacques Brel, so he opens a listening room with a bigger stage 'downtown' and calls it The Gate of Horn.

Bob Gibson headlines The Gate of Horn. People were catching on that he was creating folk music for a bigger, hipper crowd. His influence on the music brought accessibility and a modern voice, shortening the songs, and widening the audience.

In the darkness of Rosehill, sitting at the misty coffee house tables, where ghosts and the living mingle, are those who came to hear Bob Gibson sing, folks like John Lennon, Paul Simon, Gordon Lightfoot, and the music world.

It is said by some that Bon Gibson didn't just influence folk music. He started it.

***

In moonlight again, voices rise from Rosehill Cemetery, weaving alongside Bob Gibson in beauty so strong it hurts.

Another scene emerges. A young woman practices her singing in the YWCA stairwell where she stayed when she was in Chicago. Her name is Joan Baez, and some say, when Gibson brought her onstage at the 1959 Newport Folk Festival, he launched her career. But Gibson always plays that down. "Discovering Joan Baez was like discovering the Grand Canyon. Someone would have done it no matter what."

I have an old memory of my aunt's apartment, filled with the music of Bob Gibson. It would be hard to forget that time, when she put his record on to play and said, "Sure, we've met." I wonder if I could meet him too?

***

Time shifts again, illuminating the foot of a tiny stage. There, on the campus of Northwestern University in Evanston, Illinois, people sit on the floor in what feels like an old house trailer. The room is called Amazing Grace. Bob Gibson is about five feet away, singing.

Deep inside, my soul shifts and changes. I smile, because he is smiling. He is singing to the world. But with a wink, a smile and a nod, he is also singing just to me.

In September of 1996, Bob Gibson had just enough time left for a farewell party in Chicago. A week later, and he was dead.

Roger Ebert wrote, "... Bob Gibson hosted his last hootenanny and attended his own wake."

That October, a few weeks later, on a day a lot like this one, in a room set up with folding chairs, the public remembered Bob Gibson. I remember a white-haired man in a red-checkered shirt sitting behind me, clearing his throat. While other people got up to share their memories, the man in the red-checkered shirt kept his head down, talking to himself, getting ready to speak.

That man, Studs Terkel, would speak last. And I remember how he started. Four words ...

"When Bob Gibson sang ..."

Listening to Studs and it all came flooding back: that Bob Gibson command, that big guitar, that shared smile and the spotlight, that way he tells a story to touch both the audience and the larger point.

That incredible talent of making people smile, because of the way he smiles first.

Bob Gibson still sings.

From the ghost moons of October shining over Rosehill, or anywhere you live.

You can still hear Bob Gibson sing.

Anywhere you live.

Source Credit: www.bobgibsonlegacy.com

Rayray String Bean

Rayray string bean, green cap, narrow eyes
Never wears a coat
In the white winter blast
Of the Illinois prairies.
Laughs like a dribble cup.

We live in a town called Normal, Illinois
Which Rayray finds uproarious.
Waiting to write like
David Foster Wallace.

Rayray is level, smooth, and shiny like a mirror
If he just stays on his meds.
We're in Normal now,
But someday we'll graduate,
Make it to Chicago,
Where we can write like David Foster Wallace.

Rayray sees soldiers
If he skips one dose.
And the soldiers have no eyes.
And they beat with just one heart.

And they march inside his spine,
Crackling broken glass,
Ding-dong, Dorothy dead.

The soldiers are marching, little eyeless monkeys
And Rayray starts to scream,
But only if he forgets to take his pills.
That worked when we were all in Normal.

But the story took a turn
When we made it to Chicago.
There was an incident with a gun.
And now there are no pills
In the Cook County Jail.

While Rayray's parents
Breakfast in their sunroom
In Kenilworth, Illinois,
Where the coffee is served
In white bone china.

They have no son.
He is dead to them.
But they keep up on current news,
Thumbing through the Trib.

Look at this, says Ray Senior.
Says the Sheriff of Cook County
Is now the single largest provider
Of mental health in the region.

Because they're closing
All the mental hospitals.
Rayray's mom, Bitsy, takes a bite

Of her cinnamon bun.

We've got to rein in spending,
Control the deficit.
Ray Senior nods,
Looks at his watch,
Says he's got to run.

While his son sits
On a cold metal bench
With twenty-three other lost souls
Waits for the soldiers
Prays they'll come soon
And screams so David Foster Wallace
Can help him stay alive
Just one more night.

A Song of Thanks

It was not the best setup for destiny. She lived in a small town in Missouri and I lived in Chicago, and for a while, we spoke a lot by phone. She had been mentioning this guy she knew from town ... what fun they had going fishing together ... how he owned a jewelry store. With each call, her voice faded and grew more distant. I began to think the jeweler would eventually close the sale and make them a couple.

In late November, I got the call that there would be no more calls. Destiny, finally, drifted away on a warm southern wind. I could not seem to grasp the reality that she would dump me. I thought we were for keeps. She didn't even bother to say, "It's not you. It's me." That line is always good, especially when it's a lie.

Old story. It wasn't *Look Homeward Angel*, it's just I wouldn't be leaving Chicago for a trip to her mother's house in Gulfport, Mississippi for Thanksgiving that year.

I had been through this once before, left alone on Thanksgiving. Without knowing what, I knew that I had to take some action, do something. I told myself that I wouldn't be stuck around some dinner table where everyone gathered because they thought they were supposed to. I had no intention of following some genetic instinct of holidays and family and their supposed meanings, that unstoppable rhythm that people dance to without knowing it was even there.

I didn't want to spend Thanksgiving with someone just because I was supposed to spend it with them. I didn't want it to be about obligations. Even if I liked the people.

I held a photograph in my hand. It was the one she took of me in the cemetery in Asheville, North Carolina, kneeling next to Thomas Wolfe's grave. Just before she took the photo, I brushed away a speck of dirt from the granite slab. The pure mountain air felt like a cool, cleansing tonic that really could clear tubercular lungs.

I wondered if that air could make me write like him.

I couldn't imagine Wolfe as a Thanksgiving Day guest. That would be impossible. Right? Him being dead and all.

***

New snow was just beginning to fall, driven sideways by Chicago winds that blasted like jet engines revving for takeoff. I opened the door to a joint over on Wabansia, under a Hamm's Beer sign of faded neon. My greeting consisted of a shout, "Hey, close the damned door, kid!"

I wasn't sure who yelled. It could have been the bartender, faceless in the shadows at the back of the dark bar. Maybe it was the guy sitting at the bar, whose wire-rimmed glasses failed to conceal his intense gaze.

As I stomped the dusty snow off my boots and unzipped my big down coat, I looked again at the guy hunched over at the bar. I was unable to focus on him. Like a shadow, he faded in and out.

The solution was a quick drink. I ordered a beer and a Jack Daniels shot before I even sat down. I took the drinks from the still-faceless bartender, laid a ten-dollar bill on the bar, and turned to offer a toast to the guy with the glasses. Once again, he seemed to have faded away. The empty bar stool showed no sign he had ever sat there. When the bartender retreated to his corner, I felt totally alone. As that feeling reached its peak, the bar ghost faded back into view. He gave me a wink and said, "Yeah. It's me. Sorry about the whole Thanksgiving thing, kid. I know what it's like getting dumped. Me and Frenchie ..."

I couldn't help but interrupt. I knew who he was, but no way. I knew that Frenchie was his name for Simone de Beauvoir. "Algren? Really? Nelson Algren?"

"Do I look like Papa Hemingway, kid?"

"How are you ... What is ... Why am I ... What the ..."

"Easy kid, we'll let you ask your questions. But first, let's get a table. We're gonna have some company."

Algren motioned me over to an even darker corner of the bar, and that was when I saw Thomas Wolfe stepping out of the shadows, alive as could be! Wild hair, eyes darting all over the room. I could see him writing with neither pen nor paper nor typewriter. Just him fidgeting in his chair was writing!

Wolfe said, "Sorry about the Thanksgiving thing, kid. Thought I'd pop by. See if I could help. Awful nice of you to come by my grave."

"Yeah," said Algren. "We figure we can have Thanksgiving tonight. Where we come from, see, the exact day doesn't really matter too much."

"I have," I said, close to losing the ability to speak, "so many questions!"

"Well, that's nice, kid. But why don't you wait until everybody gets here."

"Who else is ..." and just then the barroom door opened. Framed with another swirl of snow, in walked perhaps the greatest of all American male vocalists, Joe Williams. As if reading my mind at the sight of my dropped jaw, he boomed out a laugh and said, "That whole being-the-greatest-male-vocalist? That's not the way Frank Sinatra sees it. But truth be told, does it matter?"

"No. I guess not. But why are you here, too? I mean this has got to be the greatest Thanksgiving night I've ever spent. And it's not even Thanksgiving night! But there is so much here I don't understand ..."

"Which is why you get to ask each of us one question," said Thomas Wolfe.

"But — why can't I ask more?"

"How about this, kid. If you asked us each more than one, it would make the story too long. Christ, kid, you already tossed in the bit about getting dumped at the beginning. What was the point of that? To make us like you more or something? Ever hear of editing, kid? Ever hear of getting to the point? Story is already too long. So, you get one question answered by each of us."

"Well sure, but I ... okay. Mr. Wolfe, I remember when I first started reading you, how many times I thought, why the hell do I want to write? I'll never, ever, ever be as good as Thomas Wolfe! So why bother? I guess that's my question. Why bother trying to write? What's the point?"

"Ok," answered Wolfe, "you ready for your answer?"

"Yes sir."

"Here's the answer: I don't know."

"You don't know? You're Thomas Wolfe! If you don't know why we bother to write — especially now, with you being dead and all — how will I ever figure it out?"

"You won't, kid. You'll never figure it out. Because the answer is a mystery. No one knows. That's the point. No one knows."

"So, what do I do?"

"You stop asking questions like that. You just write. Because here's the thing kid. When I write — and of course I still do it now — when I write, I am never alone. So, I just write. So enough on that. Nelson, it's your turn."

Nelson Algren has sold books all around the world, Hemingway considered him one of the greats.

He is still read today, but is not universally well-liked in his home city of Chicago. Toward the end of his life, he left Chicago.

I had a million questions for this teacher, but if I had to choose one, it must be, "Mr. Algren, what if people don't like your writing? Don't like or don't care. If people don't respond to your writing, what do you do?"

And he answered me, "Kid, let me ask you a question. Is this about you or about the writing?"

"Well, I ..."

"Do the right people like your stuff?"

"You mean the people who will buy it?"

"No kid. I mean the right people. That means something different to every writer. Take, for example, you. Do you remember that writers read you? Writers you respect? Remember the time Roger Ebert tweeted your stuff? Remember all the great writers on Open Salon and Fictionique? Remember how friends of Studs Terkel said Studs would have liked your stuff?

"Well, I ... yeah."

"Then that's the answer. When somebody doesn't like (or worse yet, doesn't care) about your work, when no one comments on what you do, then what do you do? You ask yourself, do the right people care?"

For a moment, the room was silent, except for the sound of the wind outside picking up even more.

"Oh. Well then, my last question is for Joe Williams. Sir, I am honored you are here, but I'm not sure why. So, my question is this: Why are you here?"

"That's an easy one, son. I'm here because good writing is always full of music. Everywhere someone talks about writing, music is there too. But there's another, more important, reason. I am here to tell you this: Every time someone writes, every time someone tells a story, it is an act of Thanksgiving. That's what it is, son. And this: When you are giving thanks, you are never, ever alone."

As I let that sink in, it felts as if the wind had stopped blowing for a moment. I closed my eyes to think about what he said, and when I opened them again, my three Thanksgiving companions were gone. I was left with their answers, Joe Williams' words echoing in my mind.

I put on my coat and opened the door to walk out into the snow, saying out loud, "Every time you tell a story, you are giving thanks. And when you give thanks, you're not alone." I thought about my Thanksgiving, the one I ended up sharing with three of my teachers. As I spoke those words into the snowy winter wind, I could hear Joe Williams sing a song of thanks.

Royko and the Bully

Like lots of unmarked street corner taverns, this one is bathed in a perpetual interior twilight and the smell of stale beer. I'd tell you where it was, but you would never find it.

When you walk in, you swear the place is empty. Nothing is moving, and time has frozen into a copper-colored stillness. You blink and scan the room again. This time you see an old man on a barstool nursing his drink. Slouching at the sink behind the bar, a ghostly bartender polishes a beer glass. As your eyes travel towards the back of the room, at the dark end of the bar, you see the ball in the air.

***

A man in a gray raincoat, face hidden in the shadow cast by a faded blue Chicago Cubs cap is rhythmically tossing a 16-inch softball just above his head, catching it, and tossing it up again. As if he and his ball are getting ready to do battle with something still unseen.

At the front of the bar, nearest the front door, hunched over a ginger ale, is old Great-Uncle Lester 'The Lip' Lapczynski. Wisps of white hair frame his bent head, and his beat-up madras sport coat breaks every law of good taste.

***

Whatever brought you into this cool afternoon darkness must have been a mistake. It's time to go. As you step away from this silent scene, into the rush of the busy street corner outside, you stop.

***

The Bully pushes open the bar room door and pauses for an unseen audience, framed in the doorway. Strutting into the room, he bellows, "Where's this Royko guy I been hearing so much about?"

The man with the softball looks up. Doesn't say a word. He just keeps tossing the softball up and down. Lester turns around from the bar and faces the Bully. "Mister Royko said he had a dog show to cover this afternoon. He sent me to meet you."

"Dog show!! I'll show you dog show! There is no dog show here. And besides, I don't do deals with errand boys. I heard Royko's the man who writes the stories, the man to see. I also got the word that he's nearby. So where is he? Is he hiding? Is he scared? If this Royko buy wasn't such a loser, he would know that I'm the only story here!"

And as he pauses for breath, the softball hits the bar and goes still. The man in the faded blue Cubs cap vanishes and a sweet, low rumble of laughter rises up from the dark end of the bar, where the man used to be.

Still the Bully prattles on. "Do you know who I am, old man?"

"Listen," the spray from Lester's lower lip splatters all over the front of the Bully's red tie and blue suit. "Far as I'm concerned, you are just another Stinky McGoohan."

"Stinky McGoohan." said the Bully, "Never heard of him. Don't know him. And if he says I owe him money, he's lying I tell you! So, you tell me now. Who is Stinky McGoohan? Is he another one of Royko's pals?"

"Who is Stinky McGoohan?" said Lester, spraying out enough spittle to water a small garden. "Let me tell you who he is. He's just a plain old bumbling backyard bully. A trash can full of rotting banana peels, coffee grounds, bluster, and fear. A guy who lives his life thinking, 'Who can I step on today?' A Stinky McGoohan is a guy who can't just win. He has to make sure you lose!"

"Aww you're talking crazy. I got no time for this. I got meetings downtown. Somebody wants to take my name off the side of the big, beautiful building I built on the river."

"Is that the building," sputtered Lester, "with all the plumbing problems?"

"I got no comment. I heard enough," snarled the bully. "If Royko ain't gonna show, I'm gone!"

And as he turned to leave, a fiery, fast pitch softball roared by, just missing the top of his head.

***

The next day there was, of course, no column in the newspaper by the late great Mike Royko.

But if you were to go to the sports page and take a magnifying glass to what looked like—to the naked eye—a pinprick of spilled ink, you'd see what looked like results from a dog show. No one was sure how they got there. Or if dog show results were what they really were.

But if you listen hard to the sounds of the right Chicago street corner, you can hear Royko laughing.

And The Blood

And the blood burbled out
Dribbled down.
Stained his shirt.

He dropped down hard head,
Smacked the soot-stained sidewalk,
Shook loose.
Slammed beneath the city street throng.

I did not see the moment
But I heard the sound
Bone on concrete
Sprawling arms convulse, then still.

Under brutal baked and cruel city sun
That said there might not be tomorrow.
And the blood burbled out
While the circles of cell phones rose to attention.

With a slow-motion-time staccato crowd moan
Yips and yaps of blind impotent orders given,
"Be careful!" "Don't move him!"
"Give him room!" "Just be careful!"

Coming in an instant that felt like forever.
The siren came ripping
Through the heat like a razor-honed knife

Through melted butter.

Here they come, the social safety net.
With lumbering certainty,
Lights flashing, seas parting,
They disembark, taking positions, checking vitals.

Street science saviors
Seeing more than the rest of us.
Making the decision
He was alive enough to move.

Looking like a worn-out wandering beach boy
Gone too long from a sad distant ocean
Swallowed by the city.

Dirty blond hair, t-shirt, jeans,
Dreams of summer waves
And a smiling surfer girl.

While resolute, plodding, street science saviors
Secure their new charge
Lifting up the sleeping beach boy.

Those social safety net people, a man, a woman
Lifting him high above the glass-cracked
Baked, tired, Chicago sidewalk.
Sliding him into their wailing flashing chariot.

I'm wondering if there'll be someone worrying

When the cracked head bloody beach boy
Doesn't make it back home on time
Tonight.

Trailing Sorrow

No one sees her face. Her head slumps down, hidden inside the scraggly beige coat that is her only real home, the one she has no money to clean, as she shuffles past on her walk north every morning.

Like a burned-out barren asteroid whose last vestiges of a trail is made of unfathomable sadness, she blends with the grey winter sunrise, a rolling trail of sorrow.

Crossing Grace and trudging silently up Hermitage, she is falling back into long past times as she passes five little houses where factory workers and their families once lived. Irish on the south side of Grace, German on the north, where men listened for the whistles at the old Abbott Drug Plant, the Choir Robe Plant, or any one of the other dozens of manufacturers that lined the train tracks of the Ravenswood corridor, where women swept their front sidewalks clean. She is remembering how, once every summer, on a Sunday afternoon, the families would take the walk to Wrigley Field.

The factory families are gone, just the little houses remain.

Downstairs in the basements of those little factory homes, hardwood beams from northern Wisconsin forests provide support.

Cassie knows where these hardwood beams started their lives as trees in the forests of Northwest Wisconsin. She knows the cherry farm off Sturgeon Bay and the Wisconsin winters. Sometimes when Cassie walks, when the wind blows fierce, she smells the moraines left millions of years ago when the glaciers came through and sculpted the Great Lakes. She knows how the Door Peninsula shines its brilliant promise in the light of bare trees. She recalls a white church on a hill overlooking a bay in a town called Ephraim.

Cassie gets confused between back then and now.

Remembering a long time ago, their tiny little farm lay in the curve of the shoreline made splendid by the sun.

Then came the war.

That's when he left for the other side of the world, a land of living hell, of deprivation, of short rations and blasted bodies. He wrote to her about his men. When the shooting pains started in her legs, followed by sharper pains, she waited still, the letters keeping her going. "You'd eat what?" she'd write back, twisted inside with the worry that he wasn't taking care of himself. He just thought about the men, writing about them, telling her that no matter where they all were in that war zone, what really mattered was that "officers eat last."

Officers eat last. Last words of his she ever read before getting the telegram.

Last of the little farm, no money for little cherry farms. Not anymore.

So, she came to Chicago to find work, like people have always come to Chicago.

No one with an ounce of sense ever mistakes Cassie for lazy. But times get harder, clouds of blame drift and wrap in smoky haze around those least able to care for themselves. Those who *have* find ways to blame those who have the least. Cassie's daily walk is eight miles, with paper-thin leather on the soles of her shoes.

At days end, Cassie's walk south takes her along Hoyne Avenue. Like Hermitage, it is the kind of quiet street where a heavy heart may feel a trace of calm. She looks left and sees people from the neighborhood talking on the sidewalks. The block seems crowded with kids and wagons and bicycles.

One time she came here to find the block taped off and she could hear music bubbling out from a party at a house where, if she had stopped to talk, she would find people who will be kind to her, welcome her to get a good warm meal on a Wednesday night. She would hear a piano playing hymns, the same songs she would remember from the cherry grove church back home. But Cassie just keeps walking.

On to nameless streets. As usual, though, no one even sees her, and no one ever knows her story. She continues her southward walk as the winter light fades on another day of hard times.

Cassie walks, trailing sorrow.

Cassie just walks.

Walkers Restaurant

We're still here at Walkers Restaurant. Here in spirit.

Oh, the buildings are gone, as are most of our neighbors. Angela and I passed decades ago. A gas station now sits where our restaurant, and Angela's little garden once held sway. Across the Irving Park Road today, you can see the remaining traces of the Selig Polyscope Corporation, a two-hundred-acre movie studio and lot. Today you can see an archway to a building where lights, stage props, and costumes were stored. Look up and you'd see a crumbling water tower casting its shadow where the sound stage once stood. And it was on that soundstage where Mister L. Frank Baum first told the stories of his Wizard of Oz.

Today his stories are known by all. But back then the only ones who got to hear the stories were those who shared a hearty midday meal at Walkers Restaurant. Then in the evenings with candlelight flickering on red-checked tablecloths of the restaurant's dining room, he'd share the further adventures of Dorothy, as winter winds would swirl the Chicago darkness.

Quite a talker, that Mr. Baum. Feeding us with his stories.

It's easier, now, to find out about him than it is to find out anything of Angela and me.

Long after Mr. Selig and his Polyscope machine operation moved west to California, someone made another movie about Mr. Baum's Wizard. In that movie, a girl from Minnesota once known by the name of Francis Gumm, sang a song called "Somewhere Over the Rainbow." No one ever forgot the way she sang that song. It's a whole lot easier to find out about Judy Garland than it is to find out about our restaurant.

Finding us is still possible, even though we're not in books, or movies, or songs. Walkers Restaurant can still be found, much in the same way Mr. Baum would have us all find Oz. At the end of a meal, chairs pushed back from the tables, the room turning dark, the only sounds are the wind and the story. Quiet now. Close your eyes. Concentrate. Listen hard.

And here we are, going back, back to how Walkers Restaurant came to be.

It begins with a whiff of oregano.

Here, outside our back door, is Angela's kitchen garden. A whiff of fresh oregano rises, like in the moment that follows warm summer rain. Almost imaginary, then growing stronger. Oregano, then basil, then tomatoes, warmly fragrant and sun-blessed. Grab one from the basket and gently cradle life's abundance in one hand.

Angela farms tiny, green, smiling herbs like da Vinci sketches in book margins. In her kitchen, she blends tomatoes and herbs into sauces tasting of the warm rain and summer sun themselves, as though they could wrap their hands together and stir the wooden spoon. Each morning, pasta is spread on her table in a white-floured haze, rolled, and cut. The sausage comes from the Lincoln Avenue shops to the east of us, and the leafy greens come from her garden outside the back door. And the bread? Fresh like a piece of heaven that could be broken off and made even better, that bread just begs you to reach for the creamery butter.

She starts every day like da Vinci. She finishes with a meal that would make the Mona Lisa smile.

For years, before the restaurant, it was just the two of us, living just east of Mr. Selig's Movie Studio in a tiny white house. Nearby factories that line the railroad chugging celery from our neighbors' farms down to Chicago, six miles south.

Then, both Angela and I were working at the stately bank that anchored the corner of Lincoln Avenue and Grace Street. We were safe.

Over time, when the celery farms got smaller, when the Clark Street honkytonks got louder, when money began flowing into our corner of the world, we began to see a problem. Working at the bank, we could see that money was going only to a small select few. And tired answers about how it's always been this way solved nothing.

Chicago was bursting out in every direction, land becoming more and more valuable. Those who owned the land, those few, began to get very wealthy. In came the money for the owners of the factories that made choir robes and trumpets and drum mallets. World shakers like Dr. Abbott, who helped change the course of medicine, lived here too. Those kinds of neighbors meant more money flowing in. New ways of thinking were to be found everywhere you looked. And there was money to be made.

Even then, there were those who owned the property past which the rivers of money would flow. Angela and I were just the ones counting their money.

As the years passed around us — at the church, in the streets, in the bank, and as the money and the people flowed in — those with the money began to speak to us politely, but only when necessary.

The newly rich banded together, whether for protection, out of fear, or simply the natural course of things. There were those on the inside and those on the outside of this new circle of wealth.

Angela and I weren't on either the inside or outside the circle of wealth. We were just two strange bankers who simply did not fit in.

One night, a letter was left on our doorstep in the darkness. It came from a member of the local church. She had disguised her name, but we bankers have ways of seeing through such disguises.

It was a hate letter, though the exact wording is unimportant. Her message was clear.

You're different. You don't belong. Get out.

So, the next morning, a Saturday, Angela and I did what we try to always do in times where thoughtful response is needed. We went for a walk. We love to walk along Grace Street, along Byron Street, over by the movie studio.

Perhaps that letter and our walk was would lead us to what was meant to be for us. And it did!

I can still see the moment when we both looked across Irving Park Road and saw the empty lot of land bathing in a shaft of surprise sunlight, both of us knowing instantly what it could be. A restaurant! Angela could cook like an angel. I could keep the front of the house. From the movie studio and the quarry just down Western Road, the workers will come for their meals. A neighborhood, families of all shapes and sizes, where no one goes hungry.

We would call it Walkers. Everyone might think it is our name, but it isn't. We call it Walkers because that's what we do whenever we have a few free moments. We walk.

There were not any restaurants nearby, closest one was Buckthorn Tavern on Elston Avenue, west of us. But Walkers would be different, not just a stop along the way, but a place to rest. To restore.

The beating heart of Walkers would be the kitchen. Open to the dining room, to our guests, to our community, you'd see Angela dancing her way around that kitchen, making meals from her family's ancient home on the rocky island of Sicily. Our guests, German and Irish, would share food from a distant world, acknowledging the meal itself as a kind of grace. With ballet-like precision, Angela would present the food as art, a framed restorative for the work-weary soul.

Perhaps I could make a few of our guests laugh. Tell a story or two. Not like Mister Baum; but I could sometimes hold my own.

When the restaurant would be full, when that smell of oregano would drift through the room and light up the faces around each of our twenty-four tables, it would feel holy.

We would fill our friends' very souls on cold winter nights, sharing times of true joy. We would feed the hungry traveler, sometimes the penniless ones, and that was fine by us, too.

Then for years, after the movie studio moved west, and the quarry closed to be replaced by a television station, and long past the time they tore down the Lutheran Seminary over on Clark Street to put up a baseball park they eventually called Wrigley Field, we stayed. We made the restaurant come alive across the years.

Then when Angela and I passed, ownership of our land got transferred to a corporation I'd never heard of. I never understood how the new ownership really came about; all I know is that lawyers were involved. The restaurant stayed open, but no one came to dine here anymore. Without Angela and I gratefully welcoming the stranger, Walkers Restaurant became a tired gray room with a bare electric cord and a light bulb hanging from an open wound in the ceiling. For a while, if you'd visit, you would find an old man slumped behind a cash register, reading a newspaper, looking up when a stray person enters, scowling, and sending the person looking elsewhere for sustenance.

From this place between the cracks of time where Angela and I now walk, I heard the words, "This is a business where everything goes through the back door, not the front."

Today, all these years later, the Walkers Restaurant building is gone and a gas station sits in its place. But Angela and I, we're still here in spirit. Our story is told in the book of Isaiah.

My people will live in a peaceful neighborhood,
In safe houses, in quiet gardens.
The forest of your pride will be clear-cut,
The city showing off your power leveled.
You will enjoy a blessed life,
Planting well-watered fields and gardens.

Walkers Restaurant is still our garden.

To those in the neighborhood who are hungry, in that singular moment just after the rain, catch a whiff of oregano on the wind, follow Angela dancing across our kitchen, and know that in spirit, we are still here.

Jack Johnson

All the gravestone says is "Johnson." And maybe that's enough.

Come by, under any old October moon, and stand quiet for a minute. Listen for the breezes come floating up from the big Lake Michigan, block out the sounds of Chicago outside the gate of this Graceland Cemetery. Stand real still and hear him talking.

His words, like quick light jabs, sting more with pleasure than pain. Like Johnson would do at the beginning of a fight when he was just playing with the other man. Stop by in October, when the leaves blaze in an orange and red whirlwind, just like one of his fights. Come by then, in the darkest part of midnight when there's only the moon, and he will be telling his stories.

Telling his stories. Stand extra still, there is something else to be seen.

Come watch him again and he'll be talking just like he did when he was in the ring and used to talk to the rich folk in the front rows.

Johnson is a fighter, kept fighting up until he was sixty-years-old. Up until those last years, up until that car crash near that little town in North Carolina that took him from this earth, he just kept fighting.

What is he fighting for?

Well, just before that car crash, Johnson walks into this little town diner, and they won't serve him a meal. The most famous black man in the United States of America. Jack Johnson from Galveston, Texas. Mama and Daddy started out as slaves. And now everybody knows his name. Johnson has more money than his Daddy ever even thought about, and this lady in the diner and her white man husband won't make him a dinner. That a good enough reason to be fighting?

What is he fighting for? He's good at it. No one better. The big fights, when twenty thousand people would be watching, Johnson dances and turns and does a little jab, a little poke. He takes his time. He believes everybody gets their money's worth watching him fight. If he gets too close to putting the other man down? He holds him up, jabs a little more, spins him around and catches him before he falls. All the while keeping up the conversation, making the jokes with the rich folks sitting right up next to the ring.

That ring? That is his real home. Johnson has some houses, some cars. He has pretty much anything he wants. But that ring? That is home, until he came here to Graceland.

Sometimes Johnson does what they call the Cellar Fights. They are the private affairs. Rich Man pay to have him come fight in front of his friends. Usually, it's in a cellar.

He gives them all as much talking as fighting in those little fights. Making sure they are smiling and a laughing and having themselves a good old time while they just wait for him to get his head bashed in.

Over the years, people write books about him. TV shows. Movies. Man, Johnson wishes he has just a little taste of the money all those folks make off him after he is gone.

'Course when he walks the earth, he knows how to take being famous and make even more money with it.

What is he fighting for? Well, he can say he likes some kind of product. And then somebody gives him money just for talking about the product! Hard to believe!

'Course that goes on after his time, too.

What is he fighting for? Well, let's see. There are folks who get pretty upset 'bout how all the women follow him wherever he wants to go. All kinds of women. Color didn't matter.

And that's where the problem comes up, 'cause color — as always — matters. Color always matters.

Now it's him and Etta and Irene. Just the three of them now. Etta and Irene? Two of his wives. And they both rest with him. Why those two? After all the women? After all the years?

Well, see that's the thing. There are some stories he never tells. Not then. Not now. Some stories he keeps to himself. Stories only for Jack Johnson. And why is he resting here with both Etta and Irene? That is one of the stories that is just for him.

That's how he keeps going all these years. All these punches. He has stories that were just for himself. He keeps them to himself. And the louder he talks, the more he makes white folks mad. The more his stories saved him. The more his private stories come to be the road to respect.

So no, he can't be telling nothing about Etta and Irene. But he can tell this ...

Come by the stone that just says Johnson. Right here, in Graceland Cemetery in Chicago. Come when the moon shines the brightest in October and the breezes are just like the feeling of the big crowd before one of his fights. Come here. Look really hard, and see Etta and Johnson, dancing in the moonlight. They are swinging and swaying. To all the music of the eternal moons of October. Then they stop for a moment. Bow their heads to each other. Irene floats in, she and Johnson take a turn, under that same October moon. There is laughing again. There is joy. There is a moment of the eternal rest when there are no more fights. The three of them join hands, make a circle in the soothing song of an autumn wind.

And for the three of them, for the circles around the circles that connect to their dance, there is respect.

That's what he is fighting for.

That is a circle of respect.

Jeannie Comes in Singing

She will be here. The church service has started. The congregation has risen, turning to the correct page in the hymnal and lifting their voices to sing. The doors to the sanctuary open, Jeannie, smiling as always, comes in singing. Doesn't need a hymnal. She already knows the words and the music. Jeannie comes in singing, finds her place in the pew, and the most ancient of hymns becomes new.

Being greeted by Jeannie is like having one's own private symphony. My father was her big brother. Family stories described Aunt Jeannie as being somewhat like her mother, a grandmother gone before I arrived. Grandmother Edith, my dad would tell me, didn't see very well. So, when she walked down the street, she would sing out a "Hello!" to everyone she encountered. Jeannie greeted the world with that same joyous hello. But with Jeannie, 'hello' was just a start.

In time compressed to fractions of seconds, Jeannie's hellos washed over like an orchestra building up to burst into the chorus of Beethoven's "Ode to Joy." The music of her greeting in rainbow colors, a joy that left words far behind, spiraling up in harmony, in rhythm, and in song — into places only music goes.

And this is just the part where she says hello.

When she greeted my father — they didn't get to see each other all that often — they would stop right in front of each other, toss back their heads, taking in the very full measure of each other. Their smiles unfolding like golden summer mornings, an almost primal hum of joy emanated from Jeannie, and the both of them exploding into shared laughter. This was a brother and a sister who could make the heavens sing with the sound of their greeting.

Jeannie, Uncle Don with Paul, Elinor, and Blake, arrived in Chicago back around the same time I finished school and settled down to start growing up. Their screened-in front porch became, through the years, a center of my world too.

Whatever the heartache, there was always that front porch. Living and dying. Becoming part of the fabric of the city. Love found, fumbled, lost then finally found for keeps. Across the golden summers, promising springs, and orange and red splendored autumns; there was always that front porch. On that front porch, when Jeannie came in singing, everyone — and there are countless numbers of us who sat on that porch — everyone swirling in her orbit had a touchstone to come home to, to gather strength, and to go out and face the world again. Don's laughter echoed down the shady street. Jeannie smiling, eyes bright, adding to whatever story was being told by anyone, making sure that the important parts would never be lost.

Don had worked for Ted Kennedy, for Jimmy Carter, then served as Chicago's Budget Director, then Professor at Northwestern, and became one of Chicago's most respected voices. The go-to guy when you wanted integrity, intelligence, and honesty.

Jeannie's job was, in the words of the poet Mary Oliver, "loving the world." And no one ever did it better.

When the job is loving the world, actions are, of course, important. But tasks, titles, or labels pale in the face of who we are. When the job is loving the world, the healing hearts and soaring souls somehow connect to that which is inevitable, that which is eternal. That eternal song that plays when needed most. Like on this one day, soon after she passed, when we had stopped by the house to check in with Don. A bunch of us on that front porch. Telling stories. Remembering.

And that's when it happened.

Don is telling the story. There's a lot of laughter. He has just about arrived at the best part of the story, when a shaft of sunbeams opens up from behind the clouds, and shines directly onto Don's face. His face lights up as if warmed by the light of ten thousand suns. All of us there that day see it. On that porch, seeing that sunlight, feeling the warmth as we all did, we knew. Jeannie is still loving the world.

Another hymn, another story, another memory. That pain of missing her, alongside that warm sun on all our faces. Listen hard. She's singing.

Jeannie always comes in singing.

PART 2: What Love Did

ROGER WRIGHT

Introduction: The World Takes a Breath

Love itself is right here in this moment, taking a stand and telling a story. These tiny stories of the morning are what love looks like.

Across the boulevard heading east, a dance of love begins. A man with wild grey hair, wearing a red-checkered shirt, grins in such a way to invite everyone in on the story. At center stage, holding his left hand, a woman smiles with such musical depth, she makes the flowers grow.

In the center of this majestic stage, designed by Frank Gehry with soaring silver steel bands poised to roll out to the sky, that man and woman are the only things keeping the whole structure grounded, held to earth, and not blasted into space.

Surrounding the couple on the stage, all the instruments are down except the first trumpet. The Chicago Symphony Orchestra is taking a break from the rehearsal for tonight's performance. As that first trumpet begins to play, the couple steps toward each other.

Bowing with surprising grace, the old man, Studs Terkel, extends his hand to the woman, Renée Fleming. She smiles. The world takes a breath, and they dance to the old song, "Dream a Little Dream of Me."

Studs whispers something in her ear, she laughs and throws back her head, and Studs does a soft shoe shuffle. The tiny improvised dance ends with their bow to each other. Still holding hands, they bow to all those tiny fleeting moments of what love looks like.

Back across the boulevard, shops begin to open their doors for the first customers of the day.

These are the stories of what love did.

The Rock Lady

Sunrise stretches up, yawning warm and golden over Lake Michigan. Across the street from stately Millennium Park, sunlight fills the cracks in the empty morning sidewalk. That early light illuminates the tiny front window of Chicago's only crystal, fossil, and semi-precious jewelry shop, making the crystals shimmer and dance. Thelonious comes walking from the south, a soft shoe shuffle thin man with a scruffy beard and a pork pie hat. Ageless, with headphones dug from a long-ago garbage bin, he plinks and plunks the piano that only he can see or hear.

Does every big city wake up the same? Could this moment in Chicago also be unfolding in Tokyo, London, or Mexico City? Could that crystal shop be just around the corner from the rushing streams of water, washing clean the ancient streets of Paris? Is there a universal rhythm to shopkeepers sweeping clean their morning sidewalks?

In front of the crystal shop, just steps from the curb, Thelonious folds his lanky, musical self into a creaky little lawn chair. He sets down a cup for the money on the sidewalk just a few inches from his left foot. Traffic is starting to build. Tulips rise along the center of the boulevard and meander along curbsides, bursting in colors of orange, violet, yellow, and red. Colors grow stronger in the sunlight, more intense as traffic increases. Fire-colored flower petals nod to travelers on the road to somewhere deemed important. Like gentle reminders that the flowers can have a value worth all the destinations in the world."

At the same time Thelonious sees the first smile and the first coin tossed into his cup, a tough little city sparrow breaks away from its pack and hovers above the locked door to the crystal shop.

As the sparrow hovers, a kind-faced woman, call her the Rock Lady, approaches from the north. She smiles when she sees the sparrow waiting. Pulling keys from her purse, unlocking the door, she opens her shop. As she does so, the sparrow zooms above her and lands inside on a beam over the door of the shop. The Rock Lady sprinkles seed on the sidewalk and the sparrow swoops down, takes a few pecks, then flies again to its perch on the beam. Out loud, the Rock Lady says for only the sparrow to hear, "I'm here for you." All day long, whenever a visitor steps into the shop, she says it again. "I'm here for you. I'm here for you."

And the sparrow stands guard.

What Love Looks Like

They are three. The father pushes the silver wheelchair, swerving, gliding, along Chicago's Michigan Avenue on a hot August day. The three cross Randolph Street and roll into Millennium Park.

The boy's eyes are blank. He slumps in his chair like a rag doll, slipping to the side. His father reaches over, rights the boy, and tries to make him comfortable.

The mother's eyes are hidden behind giant sunglasses, her mouth forms a grim straight line. Off a bit to the side, she seems to separate herself at least for this one moment. The father focuses on the task at hand. The boy flails. I watch and send out waves of welcome to this quiet corner of the park. I can only imagine. I can never really know their life.

I watch the trio on my lunch break. Watching them take a breath, I send out a silent thankful prayer for landscape architects, for those who laid the sod, and those who planted the trees. The planning and building of this little corner brought forth these very flowers to give these three a moment of perhaps some peace among splashes of quiet colors.

I imagine their story, maybe they have come from a small town or suburb for a weekend in a Michigan

Avenue hotel, spending their 'big vacation money.' 'Let the boy see Chicago,' the parents might have told each other. Perhaps the trip could be fun for them too?

Here in this park, in the middle of eight million people, there might be a chance for a person — or for these three — to find a quiet, shady spot, a moment that feels as if they are almost alone.

The moment passes. The father reaches into the pocket on the back of the wheelchair and pulls out a large bag crammed with prescription bottles, tubes, ointments, and potions.

Standing rigid, the mother's arms fold tight across her chest, signaling to the world, "I am not with them."

But then she takes off her sun glasses and I notice a difference. It's in her eyes. It's as if a curtain has been pulled back, and now a shred of her soul is showing. She glares at me and anyone else within a fifty-foot radius. Her silent message is unmistakable: her mission is to protect her family. The father shows intensity. But the mother, who at first appeared distant, now shows in her eyes, that when it comes to protecting her family, she is a warrior of unmatched fury.

Again, the boy's head slips to the side. The father rights him and then begins to prepare the feeding tube, pouring, mixing, shaking. He shoots the liquid through the tube, and it arcs into the air, landing on a tiny patch of green grass. The father prepares lunch for his child, each move practiced and deliberate. As if he's always done this. Always will. And he will never, ever, stop paying attention, making sure he gets it right. Because this is who he is. This is what he does. He takes care of his son.

The boy squirms in his chair. Watching the feeding tube held steady by the father. The green liquid flowing through the tube. Quickly, the boy is fed.

For a moment, the three pause, take another breath. Maybe the parents just want a little distance on the big trip to Chicago, and who is anyone else to judge them? The mother loves her son. She does love her son. And she will protect him with all that she is. But is it possible to have just a little bit of distance from this life?

The father watches the steady stream of summer strangers stroll by. Remembering the before-the-boy time when he and his wife stopped in crowds, grabbed a bench off to the side, and laughed while telling stories of strangers passing by. As he is momentarily lost in long ago stories, he hears the moan of his son that signals time to go.

Reaching down, he ruffles the boy's hair, unlocks the chair's wheels, and prepares to move on.

The trio starts to roll. As his head lolls again, the boy catches sight of a young woman walking by in her yellow summer dress. Her smile for the boy is as big and as real as the shining summer sun.

The boy in the chair smiles back. His eyes are alive.

And then, out loud, I say to the summer afternoon, to the parents making their way, and to the boy in the chair who still can smile,

"This is what love looks like."

Being Jill Clayburgh

Back when we thought everything was possible because we had already made all our mistakes, that's the moment when Jill Clayburgh jumped off the movie screen and landed in the sticky floor popcorn darkness of the Village Theater on Clark Street in Chicago.

Landing in the empty seat next to mine, nodding at the tub of popcorn in my lap, she whispered, "Did you get the extra butter?" And when I shot back, "Yep," she smiled deep, stuck her hand in the tub, and we both began to watch her up on the screen in "An Unmarried Woman."

Off and on she put her hands over her eyes, whispering, "Oh God, I don't really look like that, do I?" But through most of it she smiled and riffed on the plot line and the characters. "The husband had to dump me. He never would have been able to deal when he found out our kid was gay." And then later, "Okay, so I found the sensitive artist. But then six months after the movie ended, he was spending more time on his hair than I was. And let's not even talk about how the son-of-a-bitch made me carry that giant pretentious piece of crap painting down the street by myself! I got your 'I am woman' right here, pal!"

Jill and I went way back. She grew up in a big yellow house on Lake Street in the same suburb I did. But that was when we were kids. When we met again as grown-ups, she was pure, straight City-of-Chicago solid smart and one of funniest people on the face of the earth. I never really knew why it never clicked between us, hard and final.

As the opening shot of my favorite scene in An Unmarried Woman began, the Jill next to me covered her face and missed the Jill on screen, waking from sleep, dancing ballet across her bed and through the living room, framed against high-rise views of New York City. Giggling like a ten-year-old, she stuffed popcorn into her mouth, finished her coke, and started in on mine.

Both of us staring up at the screen at her eyes opening to the morning, the thought flashing though my mind once again that Jill was not the most beautiful woman I'd ever seen, until I looked twice. Look at her twice and everything changed.

"This scene," she said, "always makes me cringe."

"I love this!"

"Which part of me not being able to dance do you like best?"

"It's not just about dancing … it's …"

"Okay. Let's stop with the Mr. Deep and Sensitive right now. You saw where that went with the artist in the movie. All this popcorn! Isn't it about time we got some beer? Let's go to that bar you're always talking about. I want to see you with your other writer friends. It's so entertaining to see you debase yourself with the drunks."

I laughed and said, "Okay, okay, it's not like I haven't seen the movie at least five times already," and we bundled up to get ready for January in Chicago.

In the lobby of the theater, putting on gloves and scarves, she said, "Wait! Do you have your little writer toys?"

"What are you ..."

"C'mon, open up the backpack. Let's see who you got riding along with you tonight, as if I couldn't guess." She reached over, unzipped the top of my backpack and stuck her hand inside. Looking at the theater lobby ceiling, she said, "Show me, Algren and McMurtry!" and then pulled out battered copies of *The Man with the Golden Arm* and *All My Friends Are Going to Be Strangers*.

As we walked out onto Clark Street and turned the corner onto North Avenue, gale force icy winds of January roaring right off the thunderous lake and driving at our backs, she said, "C'mon, writer boy, give me a first line please."

"Jill, I don't know, I can't remember every ..."

The wind kept pushing us west into the winter city lights and she said, "C'mon" as she took my arm and huddled in close. "C'mon. It will help keep us warm! First line please!"

"Okay. I don't know. Let's wait till we get to the bar.

"Now tell me the name of the place we're going again."

"O'Rourke's," I said "And it will be warm."

It was only a couple of blocks, but we walked in, and it was warm. Gauzy, smoke-drenched conversation, rippling like a friendly steadily pumping space heater, filled the room. We found two seats at the bar. There were writers at the tables. Some I recognized, some I didn't. Each table was like an instrument in some orchestra, with ghosts of writers past resurrected in the dangling conversational symphony. All of it settled in as a comforting din, background music to the dancing light in Jill's eyes.

I don't remember what we talked about. I only remembered that we never stopped talking. I remember thinking Jill just might be the funniest smart person I have ever known. And if there was an edge in her, a character that might start spilling out the seams on a second's notice ... I could fix that. I could help her through it.

This was back when I thought I could fix someone else. Back when I looked hard for something that needed fixing, didn't matter if it was real or not, just so I could come riding in and fix it.

I remember looking into her eyes for hours and then I remember only sleep.

Then just sleep. Jill's eyes and then sleep.

And then my leg being shaken. Cramped. Stiff. Hearing, "Hey, old man! Wake up old man! Wake up! You done this before! You know you not supposed to be in here!

"But I always come to O'Rourke's," I say. "Hey, you know Ebert smiled at me once! And Royko, he scowled at me. Told me to get the f— out of his way!"

"Old man. This is Old Town Ale House. I don't know this O'Rourke's. I don't know these people. I just gotta clean now. So, you gotta go."

"But I have a key! A back door key! See, there was this time they were betting who could come up with the most character names from "The Great Gatsby?" And I won. And the prize was a key to the place. So, sometimes I forget stuff now. And I need to sleep. But I stay away from the shelters, I stay away from the shelters."

"Yeah, well, listen old man. You take your shopping cart and you move along now."

And as I bundle up, put my hat on and slouch toward the door, leaning over the home I keep in my shopping cart, something spills out. The man hurrying me on my way picks up what had spilled. "Hey," he says, "These are books. *The Man with the Golden Arm* and *All My Friends are Going to Be Strangers*. Are these yours? Why you carrying around books?"

At which point I stop, quit leaning on my cart, stand up straight, puff out my chest, and say, "Why do I want books? To answer that, I'd have to tell you about Jill. We watched the movie together. She was real. We even ate the popcorn together!

"You talk crazy, old man."

I smile and say, "To answer your question: Why am I carrying around these books? Here's why. Books never die. Jill might be gone.

But the books never die.

Danny Ray

Danny Ray Suitcase perches on the balls of his feet, in front of the third bench on the left in Millennium Park just off Michigan Avenue in Chicago, just before sunrise on a cold and windy morning.

All the benches are empty except for the one with Danny Ray, his five battered suitcases, and whoever it is he's speaking to that the rest of us can't see. His flushed red face and distended gut hint at some kind of medical malaise that will never be treated, some kind of pain that will never be soothed.

Danny Ray's bench is in the shadow of the giant City Christmas Tree.

The Park rivals any city park in the world. Visitors from across the globe drift by, each with their own street corner story. Laughing children run in circles. Bright-eyed lovers warm the scene. And meandering elders remember when this treasured park used to be a swampy railroad yard. The old folks remember when a train called 'The City of New Orleans' would pull into Chicago chock full of dreams. Now teenagers look up from their phones to notice 'Cloudgate,' the giant silver sculpture that everybody calls 'The Bean.'

Danny Ray sits on his bench as the hours pass. Now it's lunch time. Cold enough that people aren't lingering in the park like they do at other times. They toss lunchtime trash in the bins and keep walking, so that Danny can leave his suitcases long enough to rummage in the bins for food. The Christmas season crowds swell and build throughout the day.

Four blocks west from where Danny Ray rummages, in the lobby of the Richard J. Daley Center, a South Side choir sings about Jesus with a power and a beat that shakes the foundations of the big downtown buildings. Somehow Danny Ray can hear the hymn. So, he hums along.

In the Plaza out front of the Daley Center, a German Market has popped up, accompanied by the smell of bratwurst and onions, hot chocolate and hot apple cider, and the rising temptation to buy all the Christmas ornaments and scarves for sale that anybody's Aunt Martha would love.

Presiding over all of Daley Plaza is of course Picasso's gift to Chicago. A multi-ton steel sculpture that has no name. Leaving all who pass by with the same question, *"What is this?"*

Night comes all too soon. The shoppers and workers depart and Danny starts to rope together his suitcases. Park Security doesn't pay him any mind in the light of day — they barely see him — but it's a different story at night. Night is when he's watched. So as night settles in, Danny packs up and heads out for Michigan Avenue. He touches one of the white, concrete barriers that ring most public gathering places now, such eyesores keep the public safe from those who would drive bomb-laden cars into crowds.

Danny walks north, checking garbage bins as he goes, still having that conversation with himself. Where he sleeps will depend on what he finds, on who is near, and how well he can make himself invisible. He's been on the streets for two years now. He tried the shelters, but sometimes he forgets where they are. He remembers one that had knives. Lots of knives. So, he only goes to shelters if he can find one without the knives. One where they won't call him crazy.

Danny rolls across Randolph Street, hears Jimmy the Bird crying, "Hey brother? Got a dollar you can spare?" Jimmy sees Danny and says, "Hey my crazy talking friend, Mister Suitcase Man. I got me a pizza! I mean it is hot, it is sausage, and it is untouched. And this being Christmas Eve my brother? You and I gonna chow down on this thick crust baby with pleasure!"

So, Jimmy and Danny set out walking north then east to a patch of concrete under Lake Shore Drive where Danny might sleep that night.

"Merry Christmas my brother," Jimmy says to Danny Ray Suitcase.

Jimmy puts the pizza box on the concrete, opens it up, and what happens next in the thirty-degree cold under that highway in Chicago with only headlights for stars is something I really can't explain.

That pizza is still warm. Melted cheese, rising steam warm. "What the ..." Jimmy stares wide eyed at the pizza but doesn't finish his question. The smell of that pizza is so all-consuming that he just has to take a bite. Then Danny Ray does too. The magical warmth of that pizza, the comfort of that bubbly cheese, and the smiling scent of oregano swirling into the wind is holding back the night.

And just for that one Christmas moment, Danny Ray Suitcase remembers home.

JD Loves MM

Chances are, anyone sitting at the bar at the Cape Cod Room in Chicago's Drake Hotel that night in 1954, would have known the laughing young couple who were carving their initials in the bar as tradition dictated. Their initials might not ring a bell, but their names would.

All sorts of royalty passed through the Cape Cod Room before it ended its eighty-three-year run on New Year's Eve, the last day of 2017. Real life princesses and kings, show biz luminaries, politicians and sporting legends. Sinatra, Ronald Reagan, and Michael Jordan. Sophia Loren, Aretha Franklin, Elizabeth Taylor, Julie Andrews, and Chicago's Cusack family.

The Cape Cod Room drew in not just the famous, but the infamous, too. Frank Nitti, who came after Al Capone, had an office in The Drake for a while, so, you know he had to have dined at the Cape Cod Room.

Fine food was served in the unpretentious place built for soul-soothing warmth on the coldest winter night, seafood was flown in daily, and trout were swimming in a freshwater tank, waiting to be picked.

Of course, all that matters, but it's not what gives a place an eighty-three-year run. Maybe the place could have kept going for another eighty-three years. Hunker down to the core of this softly lit, warm nook next to a looming Lake Michigan and you'll find what's true here is the same thing that's true about any truly great element of Chicago. It's that the Cape Cod Room was a crossroads.

And anything can happen at a crossroads. Even love.

Back at the long wooden bar in the Cape Cod Room of 1954, the lighting is dim, someone is clattering dishes in the kitchen, and the place is warm on a winter night. There on barstools sit that young couple, Marilyn Monroe and Joe DiMaggio, lost in their own smiling world, generating enough electricity to light the Chicago night.

Their marriage lasted less than a year. But the love remained. When she died, he was the one who made the funeral arrangements. And then for twenty years, every single week, he sent flowers to her grave.

The initials carved into the bar, MM and JD, were still there that weekend when the Cape Cod Room celebrated its final Saturday night.

But the love story went on.

Sweet Potato Mountains

At the neighborhood grocery store, I stand gazing up at two skyscraper mountains of sweet potatoes. A woman walks up, stands right next to me and asks the exact same question that was rippling through my mind.

"What's the difference between a garnet and a jewel sweet potato?"

"That," I answer back as if answering this stranger's questions comes as natural as breathing, "is a really good question. Let me find out."

So, I ask the produce guy walking by, not even looking at the woman. In the time it takes the produce guy to answer, "No real difference at all," I notice the guy standing behind the woman.

And I notice the woman staring wide-eyed at me.

A second passes and she says, "Roger?"

It takes me at least five seconds. She's got to be at least ten years younger than I am. (Boy, was that wrong ... we're the same age.)

That same sparkle shines in her eyes as if she knows the joke and also thinks it's hilarious. Her musical laugh that resonates every rainbow color. She looks at me. Laughing. Knowing something I don't know.

I don't know who she ... "No."

I finally blurt out her name.

Nodding her head, smiling, she says "Yes!"

All I can manage, because any attempt to say something clever or even intelligible would end up as a verbal puddle on the floor in front of those sweet potato mountains, is a hoarse "No WAY."

Then she turns to the grim-faced guy behind her and says, "This is my husband, Jack. Jack, meet my ex-husband, Roger."

I shake hands with the husband. He smiles politely and I say something stupid like, "Well, you sure have good taste!"

So much for the whole 'writer' thing; I can't even speak. Much less say anything intelligent.

She asks, a catch in her voice that probably no one else can hear (except for maybe the husband), "Well, how is Rachel?" I reply "She and I ended before I even sobered up from the wedding," The line comes out hollow. Because it is so not true.

So, I grab for a fact, any fact, as if it were a sweet potato from the pile behind us. Something solid to hold on to. I say, "But I've been with the same person now for almost twenty years." Translation: "Hey, I don't mess things up any more. Not like I used to. Not like I did with you."

"How are your parents?" she asks.

"Oh. they're great. Just great. They live in a retirement community in New Jersey and ... how long has it been? More years than I can count. Do you even live in Chicago?"

"We're on the east coast. Just here to see my mom. Haven't been in Chicago in years and years."

"Is your Mom okay? Is she still in ...?"

"Yep. She's doing great. Same place! We just stopped in here by chance to pick up some stuff to take out to the suburbs. What are the odds?"

"What are the odds!" I repeat.

"This would be too unbelievable for a movie," she laughs. "Unless it was a Woody Allen movie! How are Ben and Sarah?" Ben and Sarah are my niece and nephew.

"Oh, Ben just got married!"

She puts her hand over her mouth. Then down to her knee. "He was this tall the last time I saw him! And Sarah?"

"She's an herbalist. In California"

The capacity for asking questions begins to return along with the feeling of blood in my extremities. The Husband is clearly not enjoying this little scene. It could not have been easy.

We chat for maybe a minute or two. Mostly about the coincidence. "It was really good to see you again," I say to her.

That's when it happens. She opens her arms to give me a hug. And here's what rushes back:

Deep into the heart of one summer night, we start running.

We park the car within fringes of hearing, the music streaming out from the stage of Poplar Creek, a big outdoor arena on what used to be the outskirts of Chicago. The traffic was bad. We are late. Running faster now. And in the distance, we hear the band, Dire Straits, skating over their song. 'Romeo and Juliet.' Like flying, we run. Zigging and zagging around cars, like the rushing river of our lives around polished stones.

Running, but still wary of slipping, looking to step on one slick river rock before stepping to another. Reaching that next rock, not falling face first into the river. We had to get to our seats before the song ended. Before we heard that one line.

Memories of running flow into another in that nonsensical way dreams flow and fade.

Now there is no sound.

While she sits quiet on the basement stairs, two pals and I are moving my stuff out of that deathly sad house we had bought on Carmen Street, that house like a gothic dungeon. After I leave, she endures that night when the squirrel chewed its way inside the house.

Back to right now, to the present in the grocery store, in this moment that would once again be the last, I think …

She was alone in that empty house. I was gone.

"I am sorry, I am sorry, I am so, so sorry. I tried so hard to never let you down."

From the sorrow of that dark and empty house where none of the walls ever got painted, that house where no one breathed. Back to the dream of running, back to that parking lot at Poplar Creek.

We still hold hands, running though that parking lot. The river's wild and we don't have much time. Streaming towards that music. We toss our tickets to the gatekeepers and scramble down the aisle. The song is still playing. Mark Knopfler is still singing. We get a firm footing together, on one more slippery rock. We jump as hard, as far, and as breathlessly high as we can and land in our seats, just as Knopfler sings her name and a line about reaching for the stars ..."

How true that was.

And we are back at the foot of the Sweet Potato Mountains.

A long hug goodbye. A short wave. A nod to the husband.

And the circle closes.

Tina Fey's Gyros Place

I'm in The Athenian Room, perched at a small table next to the exposed brick wall, underneath a mural of a sunlit blue and white hand-painted Greek fishing village. It's morning in the mural. But outside the front window at The Athenian Room, it's a warm summer evening, with people strolling through the soft twilight of Webster Avenue.

Alex, the owner, looks out on the room, nods at me, and accepts a nod in return. I wave away his offered menu. His eyebrows rise, I acknowledge the gesture, and he leans over the front counter to tell the grill man the order is for gyros, fries, and a coke.

Getting hungry, I close my eyes and imagine I'm a fisherman from that mural on the wall. Looking down on The Athenian Room. Remembering just a few of the threads that spooled out and connected this happy place to eat with Chicago's homegrown cultural force — improvisation for the theater.

In my mind, Tina Fey is about to walk in the door. She will be ordering the Greek chicken.

In the time it takes for her to order and eat a meal, I could barely even begin to make the connections that play out from *Improvisation for the Theater*. I could just get started on the scenes that would wind their way off midnight stages set only with two chairs, past Second City alumni lists, Saturday Night Live reruns, memories of John Belushi, and Stephen Colbert just last night. Scenes that settle in the corners of everyday lives far from show business. Such a presence, such performances can save people, change them. Getting us to celebrate the connections between people. Prompting us, after a lot of hard work, to join in to what's at the beating heart of Improv.

The essence of Improv is Truth.

I have been around The Athenian Room since the early years, before there was grey in Alex's beard. In those years, as the sun rose over the lake and I finished my overnight shift, I would jump off the shuttle bus on Halsted Street, grab a newspaper from a machine, and find — before taking my seat — my coffee poured and Alex making the $1.99 two eggs, toast, and bacon breakfast.

Lost in thoughts of those brighter days, when sunlight poured through the third-floor window of the tiny apartment in the yellow brick building, drinking in Saul Bellow, Mike Royko, and Bill Brashler as if they and all the other Chicago writers all rode in on the morning light.

With my head lost in the books, and my memory entwined with imagination, I might not have even noticed the three people seated at the round table behind me. I didn't know when they came in, what they looked like, or anything about them until they stop talking.

That's when I notice the intensity of the silence. Dropping a napkin, I shoot a look. Framed at the table are two young women and a man. Their conversation had been bubbling over with laughter, when all three do something remarkable. They all listen. Listen to each other as if listening was a contact sport. That silence you hear is the echo of someone listening. Listening like it was a thing you could put on the table right next to the Greek fries smothered in the juices of the gyros and flavored with a touch of vinegar.

Listening like no one else listens is the first key to improvisation. Imprinted on my very soul.

I hear one of the women is called Tina. But I can't really get a sense of who these three are, so I shift my chair. My second glance shows something else at the foundation of improvisation for the theater. There are no stars. Not here. Not now. Learning the craft demands that there be no stars. Because every action depends on someone else. The three fellow diners conversationally bounce off each other like three silver pinballs. But no one is a star.

I look again and swear one of the women notices me noticing. And is giving 'a look' back! I put that down to wishful thinking, but I had seen in her eyes a unique kind of intelligent awareness. Intelligence that comes from not being scared.

Now the boundaries of imagination, memory and time are gone. There is only me and the trio at the other table.

Their conversation deepens. I listen harder. I begin to hear names that are rarely, if ever, tossed into the spotlights of Saturday Night Live. I hear the name Neva Boyd. A woman born in 1876. Friend of the pioneers of social service, Julia Lathrop and Jane Addams. Neva Boyd, who figured out that encouraging children to play games with each other made for deeper, richer lives.

Imagine what it would be like to live in a time when people didn't know that? Oh, maybe they knew it about their own kids. Neighbor's kids. But not about the children of the immigrant, the children of the vulnerable.

The laughter at the table next to me stops for a moment as the food comes and you hear the gasps of awe. Years from the night I last sat at that table, another author and I would co-write a book on customer service. That book was shelved in favor of another that became a New York Times best seller.

Maybe a good business decision? Not so good for me. Good thing I could improvise with what came next.

As I listen to the three at the next table, no one is talking about 'me.' You hear the name Viola Spolin, author of *Improvisation for the Theater*. She took Neva's work to the next level. Spolin's son, Paul Sills, pushed it forward. The Compass Players, that University of Chicago troupe which evolved into The Second City, put the work on stage. Tossed across the table in a quiet awe, I hear the name Jo Forsberg. Del Close is mentioned and somebody laughs. Charna Halpern, Linnea and Eric Forsberg, and Tim O'Malley all draw smiles. Now heads around the table are all nodding. The names keep flowing, the circle of community expands and it becomes clear that the third key to improvisation for the theater is the deep history of this cultural force. Chicago's only real claim to have developed a unique cultural force. First listening, then working without stars, then acknowledging history. A superstructure springboard that spawns and nurtures talent.

Tina Fey, bubbling up with unquestioned inborn talent, has a river of history behind her. She can trace that all the way back to a woman born in 1876.

The sun is starting to go down on Webster Avenue. The people at the next table are finishing their meal. Alex looks over to me with a glance that says, "Hey! I need the table."

All are back out on streets of a city summer night.

Just a few blocks north on Lincoln Avenue is The Players Workshop. This place is for those not destined for the main stage of Second City on Wells Street. At Players Workshop, you can pay to learn the craft of theater improvisation. And maybe, even if it's just for a moment, feel the art. Feel some truth. Feel some history.

I step up the pace so I won't be late for my class. Now arriving and opening the door, I am early. Thirty some years early for a Tim O'Malley Workshop from the future. A future that is happening right this very moment. As if a door through time has opened up for my friends and I to create something out of nothing.

Improv is alive!

Scene.

Street Corner Dreams

See that red plastic shopping cart from the Target store? See how it's padlocked to the street sign outside the boarded-up Blockbuster Video?

Yeah. That red cart belongs to me.

Most people don't even see it. Nobody wonders how the cart got from the store to the street. No one wonders what's under the dirty blue tarp that covers all the stuff inside.

Which is fine. Because it's nobody's business.

Where do I keep it at night? That's nobody's business too.

Tell you one thing. I keep nothing in a shelter. I can tell you that. I have seen rusty can opener knife cuts to the chest, screwdriver slashes to the face, stomped-on fingers from fights just to get into a shelter. Crazy folk don't even know what they are fighting for. Crazy people fight their way in then once they get in, they go fighting their way out. Even in the shelters where they keep the lights on all night. I've seen real fights. The kind you don't talk about. Blood flowing like wine. Splattered on the dirty grey snow.

So, I have a hiding place for me and my stuff at night. It will last as long as it lasts. I don't really think about it that much. The nights come early, with winter in the winds. So, I unload my stuff and lock the cart up tight by the time the sun goes down.

Of course, I'm not talking about unloading my picture. That old snapshot? That always stays with me. It got a little messed up when I stuck an old bar of soap next to it in the pocket of my jeans. But never mind about that. I can't see it all that well anyways. My eyes ain't the same since that day a crazy pick-up driver almost hit me, my glasses came whipping off and shattered on the street. Had to say goodbye to seeing straight.

But I remember that snapshot so well that it doesn't matter that it's all torn and blurry now. More like a dream than something you could hold in your hand.

I remember that moment when the picture came alive.

***

It was a lifetime ago. The woman in the snapshot is bending over some tomato seedlings, surrounding them with basil. The whole north side of Chicago seems to have community gardens everywhere. Ours is in Old Town, across from a Standard Gas Station and Lincoln Park, where the hippies long ago had tried to set up camp.

It is spring of course. Our two garden plots adjoined. But there is something in the wind off the lake that says our two little plots were just meant to be next to each other across many springs.

I walk up behind her. She is on her knees, wearing short cut-off jeans and a yellow top. She stands up, turns, puts her hands on her hips, smiles and says, "Hey, why don't you take a picture. It lasts longer."

So, I do.

And the camera catches her smile as she says, "I can't believe I just told a total stranger, 'Take a picture, it lasts longer."

"Because, you don't usually talk in lame clichés?" I say.

"Yeah," she says, looking at me hard, "that would be the reason!"

We start talking gardening, summer, the other people who had the plots, the conversation like some sort of river that just never stops. As the sun comes up higher, we traipse across Wells Street to Nookie's Restaurant and have pancakes, bacon, eggs, orange juice, and a lot of coffee. A breakfast like we had known each other forever.

***

Over the years, buildings go up where the garden used to be. No more scraggly carrots yanked out of the urban soil. But I hold on to her snapshot. Years of dwindling chance meetings. A White Sox game where I obnoxiously lecture her on the evils of smoking. That Jill Clayburgh movie where she does the play-by-play and roots for the weaselly investment banker to kick the bearded artist's ass. I remember a postcard from Japan where she just wrote, "Watching lesbian sumo wrestling. Wish you were here."

But I never let go of that picture of her face. Oh, it was a long, slow march to living on the street. Everything changed. Sometimes it got to feeling like I lost a little piece of my brain every day.

But I always hung on to that snapshot. That picture of her never got old. Even when we ran into each other for that one last time.

The last time I saw her just before she saw me. Bending over from the rear. This time in the recycling bin. Outside a 7-11 store.

Straightening up and laughing, she says, "He finds her in a recycling bin. Little heavy on the symbolism, don't you think?"

"Maybe just a tad."

And with that we fall in step together as if we always had been, always would be too. Like the snapshot, nothing changed.

How it ends this last time is that I decide, with virtually no thought at all, that marriage to another woman would be the answer. Clear thinking is not my strong suit.

Then one day when the woman in the snapshot calls to ask if she should take a pound of chuck out of the freezer for dinner. I say no. And I never make it over for dinner.

And that's what left me with just that picture of her face.

Which is why, when I see that face today, pulled out of the past, unchanged, and still young, just as I am unlocking my red shopping cart, when I see that face, it all comes flooding back. The garden, the breakfast, the stolen moments through a lifetime. I see her face again. As if she never got old.

It's early in the shadows of an empty Sunday evening. A lone young woman is walking her dog along Lincoln Avenue. Both the woman and her dog are curious, young, and calm. She is wearing jeans and a baseball cap. She has that same amused look in her eyes — like the woman in my snapshot.

And that dog-walking woman has her face. Straight from my snapshot. Like a street corner dream of time standing still. The exact same face.

Now most people, when they pass this old man pushing the red shopping cart through the streets and alleys, most people don't see me. Some pretend not to see me. But most really do not see me. Either way, most people can't be bothered.

But as this young woman passes, with her dog she looks up. She looks up and sees me. As if I was still here.

And then she smiles.

Just like the woman in the snapshot, she smiles.

And I go to lock up my shopping cart safe for the night.

Glass-Eyed Lady

Her glass eye didn't really bother me, but killing me off with a heart attack? That was a problem.

Is this a true story? Hard to say. Truth gets hazy when it's searched for too hard.

I was looking for true love. Or — like the previous marriage — some reasonable facsimile. But, like truth, finding true love is tough if it means knowing the difference between what someone says ... and what one wants to believe.

Fortunately, there are a few facts. The look on my pal Larry's face of combined horror, admiration, and then pity in one fleeting glance when he said, "You did what?"

"I put a personal ad in the Reader."

Men Looking for Women ads (what people did before online dating sites) with the 'me looking for you' ads were big. The Reader was a free paper, woven into the social fabric of parts of Chicago.

But neither of us knew anybody who actually did this.

The ad said something about looking for a woman who appreciates what it's like to live in Mayberry, but won't actually do it and who knows all the words to an old Sonny and Cher song.

I hadn't yet learned that talking in code is a problem. Perhaps things might have gone a bit smoother on the romance front if I stopped seeing life as a story being written.

Larry's first question, after several seconds of silence and a couple of long, long drinks of his giant Weiss beer was, of course, "So did anybody respond to you?" Emphasis on the word you.

"I got seventy-five responses!"

"Get out. Bullshit you did."

"No, I really did," and I was proud of that. This would predate me figuring out that more is most often not better.

"But were they like psycho weirdos? Women just out of prison? What? What? Do not tell me you went out with seventy-five women. Like ever. In your life."

"I called back twenty, and I went out with five."

"What about those five?"

"Well, there's one I'd like to see again."

"Nice looking?"

"No but . . ."

"Funny? Rich? What?"

"She has a glass eye."

"Roger, you are one weird ass mother." He shook his head in that knowing way friends do.

"And ..." I continued with the other part, the inevitable punch line we both know was coming. "She's a writer."

"Of course, she is," he summed up. "She's perfect for you. A glass-eyed writer. Does she really have a glass eye?"

I answered indignantly, "Of course!"

All I really knew for sure is that one eye sometimes looked off in a different direction. More stationary. I didn't really know. But she said she had a glass eye. And I never actually saw anything she had written ... but ...

I really wanted to her to be a writer.

I didn't even know the word 'edgy.' But if I did, it's what I would have used to describe what I was looking for. And she might have been edgy. Our first date was at Miller's Pub. Nestled under the El tracks in the Loop. Pictures of all the famous people on the walls. Tall red vinyl booths and waitresses named Shirley who had seen it all.

What happened on that first date? Stacy and I figured out that we really did like each other.

As I would come to learn later, a woman can make quite an impression if she knows how to show up unannounced at the door of a guy's apartment, wearing only a raincoat and heels.

And don't forget. She was a writer. Just like I wanted to be.

We started spending time together. Every now and then I asked how her writing was going, but there was always some incomprehensible explanation about a problem with the publisher. We passed some seasons together, even a Christmas break when neither had family obligations. Knowing we wouldn't always be together, we gave each other ornaments for future trees, future loves.

At least, that's what I thought.

I often didn't hear from her for a few weeks or months. I didn't think much about it … on again, off again, whatever. Then one day in the spring, as I was walking into my apartment, I heard the phone ringing. Ran to pick it up, and heard, "Hello Roger, it's me, Melanie? From St. Louis! Stacy's best friend? I'm so excited to talk to you in person! Listen. Our plane is due in next Friday and we are so excited about your wedding!"

And that's where it got weird.

Because the only truth I knew about in that statement was that my glass-eyed friend's name was Stacy.

I had no idea who Melanie was. Wedding?

A cold, slimy, shivering snake of fear coursed through my very soul as I stood looking out the window onto Roscoe Street with the phone in my hand.

Melanie chattered on. She said she loves the ring I had given Stacy. Several weeks earlier, she had been in Chicago helping Stacy go shopping for a dress. She was so pleased that her best friend had found someone she wanted to marry. In shock, feeling my insides being eaten by a kind of dread felt never before or since, I told Melanie that I had no idea what she was talking about. Stacy and I were friends, but that was all.

"You're the Roger who is the executive with the phone company right?" she asks.

"Yeah."

"So, I don't understand?" she said.

"Me neither."

We ended the call and I started trying to reach Stacy by phone. She had always had housing issues, and she moved around a lot. Sometimes she didn't have a phone. I wasn't able to reach her that day. The weekend passed, and still no Stacy. No word at all.

All through that weekend I felt like a silver pinball bouncing between comedy, creepy, and bewilderment.

Finally, on Monday, I called her workplace and spoke to her boss. The boss said that Stacy was not there. "She had to take a few days off. It was really sad. Her fiancé, some guy named Roger, had a heart attack. And they're not sure if he's gonna make it."

(Roger?)

"Not sure he's going to make it?"

"Yeah, and they were just getting ready to move to Dallas."

Dallas? I thought. I HATED Dallas … I would rather die than move there, and then I remembered that, supposedly, dying was what I was doing.

"That's where he was being transferred," the boss continued. "But now all their plans are on hold."

I thanked the boss and ended the call. Called a few more numbers where Stacy might be found, but she wasn't.

And I never saw her again. That was it. I never knew whether she killed me off with the heart attack, or if I somehow pulled through.

***

A few weeks later, Larry and I were walking to our cars after work one day. When we reached the edge of the parking lot, Larry said, "I'll tell you what, Roger. I'll stay over here, and you go on over and start your car … just in case anything's wired to that ignition. We wouldn't want the world to lose both of us, would we?"

Under the Cheering Stars

"Hey look! Something tiny and green is growing in the tar!"

I pop my head through the open trap door to the roof, pausing just for a moment before hoisting myself up. She is sprawling on her stomach in blue jean cutoffs and an old University of Wisconsin t-shirt of mine that she sleeps in a lot, peering over the side of the faded red blanket, and staring at something green and tiny that I can barely see.

"So, mold is exciting to you?"

She flips over on her back, and sticks out her tongue, "More exciting than you!" Then she smiles big and holds open her arms. Coming to her, I exhale for the first time that day.

"So? Tell me, tell me, tell me! How was your day?" she asks with a wide-eyed urgency and full expectation that the answer will include — at the least — a Shakespearean legend.

That's how it is. Up on that roof is where the only demands on us come from the mysteries of uncountable stars. Everything is possible. Starlit love right now. And a golden path of endless tomorrows.

Our flat is four floors up in an old red brick apartment building on the corner of Webster and Racine. The north side of Chicago, old Italian guys sitting on the street in front of corner grocery stores, Vic's Sub shop across the street, the local tavern, quiet neon. A storefront bookstore. Down the block, in the back of a Mexican market, homemade burritos and tacos. A few blocks' walk south to Armitage for Romano's Italian Ice with chunks of sweet/sour lemon. All telling every story one could need on a warm and windy summer night.

Hand holding, young, she and I have the roof.

Five of us rent the top two floors, reminding me of the rambling big white house near the campus in Wisconsin. Somehow that place had flowed into this Chicago apartment with the tall ceilings, huge windows letting in artist's light, and access to the roof. I remember none of the details how that happened, exactly. Did I sign something? Pack a moving box? No clue.

The five of us are made up of one couple, one almost-couple, and me. Andy and Marissa are the couple. Andy is slight, funny, quick and most likely will do something someday that means lots of money, probably a lawyer. Marissa's dad is a famous political guy, though one would never suspect it, knowing her and her friendly, down-to-earth ways. Zak and Lucy, they are the almost-couple. Both are artists. Zak's bedroom is the entire top floor, unfinished, unheated — even in Chicago winters — unheated. His bed hangs by four silver chains from the rafters. Swinging in the wind.

I am the odd man. A Special-Ed teacher in a flannel shirt with rolled-up sleeves, jeans, and gym shoes. Part time job at the bookstore, because Andy knew a guy. Eating $1.99 breakfast at The Athenian Room: two eggs, bacon, toast, and coffee.

Her? The first time I saw her was in that loud, smoky place across from Wrigley Field. What she saw in me that first time, it must have been some sort of miracle from a star. Because we are not the picture of a couple. She is an Old Town condo - designer business dress - right shoes - cigarette smoking girl who says to the barrage of pretty boy wannabes things like, "I'm in finance."

How we happened? She told me she was in finance. I snorted derisively and said, "Really, I'm in futures." She laughed, and that was it.

It didn't take us long to discover the roof. The other two couples have never been all that interested, so — almost always — we have it to ourselves, just the two of us and the stars. Especially as the sun drops in the western sky and the orange glow simmering twilight rises blending in tune with the city lights and the distant hum and cry of other people's lives so far down below. We lie on our backs and she talks through her day, popping up to swing around and ramp up the story, because a day is not complete for her until she talks it through. When she gets excited at some part of the story, it's like a full court press: she roars down the gym floor, leaps for the jump shot, nails it clean, and nods to the cheers of the moon and stars.

In the night glow of the city, on the roof, just the two of us lie hidden from any other human eyes. The strong, wild music of our love is heard only by those stars, the echoes carrying through time.

Music billows into the lines from Carole King's song about wishing on the roof.

That day I came up to find her staring at the green mold, I had news.

Looking in her eyes with that inner tremble I sometimes get when I think about not being able to look into her eyes, I say, "I quit. I'm not a teacher anymore." I fist-pump up to smash a star, and say, "I'm gonna do it. Gonna go corporate. I am selling out big time."

"What are you talking about? You didn't really do that. You're a teacher!"

"I can do it. I know these things. I'm older than you."

"Yeah," she laughs. "And so much more well-adjusted."

"You know what I make. Teachers never make money. I get some sort of corporate job … I don't know. Think about when we're really old. Like fifty or something. Who's gonna have the money, the corporate guy or the teacher? I mean, c'mon, you're in finance!"

"You're gonna be what, a solutions consultant? A branding manager . . ."

"Rodeo clown …" I say.

"I guess it could be worse, I could be in love with a mime. You don't have any mime plans, do you?"

Which sends me laughing, then she catches it, and we almost forgot what we were talking about.

"Hey," I say, "Should we all say a prayer to shareholder value?"

"I guess being safe … not having to scramble in our golden years … I guess that's not a bad thing, is it?" she says very quietly. "Maybe a corporate job is what you should do."

Then she gives me a very long look, punches me in the arm and takes my hand. Lying on our backs, on that roof.

Under the cheering stars.

ROGER WRIGHT

PART 3: Hope Remains

ROGER WRIGHT

Introduction: Finally, There is Gratitude

The *Hope Train* runs easy in the Chicago summertime. Rolling into town from every direction. Stopping at every address. Lingering just long enough to capture a moment of raw pain; joyful celebration; or, despite private terrors, the pure astonishment of awakening, facing the day, and getting to work. *Because there is hope.*

The whistle of the *Hope Train* sounds, reminding us that, above all, Chicago is a crossroads. Inside its patchworked core, something like seventy official neighborhoods, hesitantly hand-sewn together, lie branded by boundaries galore, labeled by whoever has the power to draw the map.

And when that whistle blows, stories take shape, born of the countless connections between all of us, unfolding in patterns shaped from the rhythm of that *Hope Train*. Such a connection is told in *Broken Dish Hopes*, the story of a momentary encounter between a political candidate and a kitchen worker. Another such connection tells how music builds bridges, in *Dear Keith Jarrett*. The connection between a young man and his future, is told in *Becoming an Inventor*. Even the brutal connections of income inequality and racism are told in the story, *Dirty People*.

As the *Hope Train* rolls out of the warm and windy summer rains, it enters Chicago's most spectacular season. Blazing colors of autumn are painted in October's crimson, burnt orange, and gold. When the bare trees of November make charcoal sketches on gray skies, this train re-connects us with gratitude. The frosty gales of winter will swoop into the city in due time, and spring is a lovely promise, but it is in autumn when the *Hope Train* calls us to be thankful. In gratitude's holiday story, *Thanksgiving Alone*, we count our blessings, not our losses.

Listen to the Hope Train pickin' up speed.
Coming home from the distance
  of a train track horizon.
Come on back to Chicago. Where hope remains.
No matter what your trial or pain,
  in Chicago, hope remains.

This Corner of Chicago

A church anchors the corner of Hermitage and Wilson, wearing earth tones of quiet pride. As the doors are thrown open, "Shall we gather at the river" accompanies the congregation streaming into Sunday morning sunshine. Their laughing joy bounces off the day in green tree wonder. This recently restored church awaits its next hundred years in understated Protestant dignity.

Across the intersection, through a gated lawn, stands the Abbott mansion, also done up for a new day. Dr. Wallace Calvin Abbott, who changed the course of what it meant to practice medicine, lived here.

The neighborhood spreading from this corner was once swampland, perfect for celery farms. Then came the factories, like the ones south of here, which produced such goods as timpani mallets, drum sticks, and choir robes. Now, it boasts painted Victorian homes perfect for a movie set with Judy Garland, sashaying by wearing a long dress and carrying a parasol.

On these streets, young Bob Fosse first danced. Marilyn Novak changed her name to Kim because Hollywood already had a bombshell named Marilyn

Monroe. And they couldn't have two Marilyns. So, Marilyn Novak became Kim Novak.

On these streets, just around the corner from the Schulhof Plumbing Supply, a stately old green three flat still stands. That's where Carl Sandburg sat in his tiny apartment and wrote about "Chicago, city of big shoulders."

The street corner stories here span farming, the railroad, manufacturing, medicine and movie stars.

Hope that reaches out to every corner of Chicago.

Hope that remains.

Broken Dish Hopes

Underneath the Hotel Allegro in Chicago, in a mostly empty kitchen corridor, Barack Obama leaned against the wall, alone, and checked his watch. Nearby, a bus cart jammed with dirty breakfast dishes waited to be washed.

In the dining room above, his introduction was winding down, and in ninety seconds, he'd get a running start for the stairs and go bounding up two at a time to spring into the good-sized room for one last stop on this campaign for U.S. Senate.

As he stood alone; the smoke-filled, back-room, cigar-chomping, nod-and-a-wink echoes of generations of Chicago politicians all paused for one eternal moment and took a look. These generations of dark and shaded political men knew that, later that night, Barack Obama would be in front of a room ten times the size of the one in the Allegro. He would be thanking everyone. So, they paused for one quick glance.

Santiago Cruz, fifty-two-years old and smiling like the Columbian sunshine even when he thought himself alone, carried a grey plastic tub of dirty coffee cups and saucers. He didn't notice the tall, thin man waiting on the other side of the bus cart of dishes.

As he swung his grey tub up over his head to plunk it down on the top of the cart, Santiago looked across and saw the quiet man smiling. In the space of a second, Santiago wiped his hands on his pants and took the other man's outstretched hand.

As Barack leaned in towards the man to shake, he bumped his shoulder hard into the cart, spilling all the stacked dishes to the floor. As they shattered in a million pieces, a jarring pain shot through Obama's shoulder, a pain so sharp he winced and bowed his head.

Wincing in pain with no clear thought at all, Obama instinctively got to his knees to begin picking up the shattered dishes.

Santiago, stunned by the crash, stood for a moment and looked down at the man on his knees picking up the dishes. Then, joining him on the floor to do the same, Santiago heard the applause from the dining room upstairs and, at the same time, the beep of the other man's cell phone going off. Santiago Cruz and Barack Obama, both kneeling on the floor, their faces a foot apart, looked straight at each other and another kind of recognition registered on Santiago's face.

Though he had been smiling before, as Santiago ALWAYS smiles, the smile took on a deeper tone. Something changed in that smile — and there was a tone of sadness in that smile for just a moment, then hope flickered, and his eyes lit up with a new brightness as he said, "OBAMA! OBAMA OBAMA!"

Becoming an Inventor

Whispering, so as not to wake your other mom, I only saw you once, for an instant. You were two months old then, today you are twenty something, one of the forty thousand California children of gay parents heard of on the news. We've never really met, so I could only imagine you strong, smart, and smiling with the promise of holding the world in your hands one day, not letting go. On this spring morning, like that one long ago, I sit with the faith (if faith is the belief in all that can't be seen) that you turned out wonderfully. And that whatever you decide to do with his life, you will do it well.

That morning long ago, I drove the Bay Bridge from San Francisco into Berkeley, with shimmering sunlight making diamonds on the water, with the golden power of the bridges, with every promise ever made, with breath made new by ocean air, and the radio played that old Rolling Stones song about not always getting what you want. On that early morning, almost Easter, University Avenue lay empty, where Kerouac's and Ginsburg's smoky words once prowled and preened on jazz fueled nights.

I found your house on a quiet street, an ivy-covered, rounded cottage, perhaps a picket fence, and two identical cars in the driveway. Your mom walked out to greet me. She was smiling. I said, "You look just the same." She smiled deeper and said, "Well, you're a liar." And I remembered how that smile once could make my very soul whole.

Inside the little house, a home where a family lived, was warm and safe. Your other mom slept behind a closed door. That moment of seeing you, then tea shared in blue ceramic mugs in a garden out back. Your mom sat straight up, perching like a therapist ready for work, looking out with wary but friendly eyes. In that way people have when there is so much to say, catching up on twenty years over a carefully planned half-hour visit, I knew I could never say it all.

There was a photograph of your mom and me standing on the railing of a front porch in Wisconsin, back when she was twenty something, like you are now. In the garden in Berkeley that morning, I asked your mom if she still had that photograph, too. She told me she did.

Sometimes a picture can say more than the words.

No child really wants to know everything about who their parents were before they arrived. Especially from a stranger. And so much of any story finds its true heart in what's hidden deeply between the lines. Fictional truth can be important too.

But, as your mom said more than once, there is a literal truth. She told me she wanted to be an inventor.

I loved that. An inventor.

It conjured images of discovering something new. Standing on the precipice of a million new springs where the term 'gay marriage' is an ancient relic replaced by the term, 'marriage.' Being an inventor means being a part of this whole sweeping promised land of this shared country, and the planet around it, and finding or pioneering something new that leaves some small speck better than when we arrived. My wish for you is that you take that feeling of wanting to be an inventor in whatever way you choose and use it. Standing on your own front porch, looking out at what your world is now; having the two moms you've had, I have faith that you will be part of that continuing renewal, part of what joins us all. I hope that, like your mom, you will want to be an inventor.

Part of this planet, in spring.

Part of this promised land.

Writing for Hope

Biff and his new wife Blythe were standing in the Starbucks line. If he turned around and saw me, he'd bring up the 'writing for free' thing. Because that's what he always did. *"Hey champ! You still writing for free?*

The question went back to our college days when Biff, for the life of him, could just not understand why I did not want to be an investment banker and make oceans of money. Now that question was the only thing he had to say to me when we ran into each other. So, he repeated it. This time I ducked my head and tried not to breathe. Hoping he would not see me.

It didn't work.

Biff was decked out in a seersucker jacket, linen slacks, and deck shoes. His black hair was slicked back. Blythe, next to him, blonde, tanned, toned, and wearing a wicked grin that said to every man in a twenty-foot radius, "Maybe you're next and won't it be fun?" reached the counter. She handed the slack-jawed barista a pound of coffee, smiling grandly. The baseball-sized diamond on her finger caught a shaft of sunlight which bounced off the silver espresso machine, temporarily blinding the barista. Dropping a pitcher of boiling milk on his arm, he screamed out in pain, "I'm an actor! I don't need this shit!"

Feigning politeness, Biff and Blythe turned away from the scene of pain and that's when Biff saw me. Eager for a distraction he asked, "Hey stranger! You still writing for free?"

I shrugged. Changing the subject, I asked, "Been traveling Biff?"

"We're just back from Cabo. A little romantic getaway for me and the little lady here."

Blythe giggled.

Both of them now putting on their 'thoughtful parents' faces as Biff continued, "but this summer, we're taking the kids to Paris. We figure it's time for some culture now that they are three and four."

"That's great Biff. You too Blythe. Well, gotta get back to all that free writing. See ya!"

Walking out the door, and congratulating myself on the quick exit, the thought struck me that maybe there was a point buried beneath Biff's $100 haircut. Maybe Biff was on the right track, but he just had the question wrong. Maybe the important question was, *"Why write?"*

Was it money? I love the stuff. Wish I had more. I wake up at four in the morning a lot and think about all the ways I can get more, worry about not having enough.

If money were my only goal, maybe I would have more. For whatever reasons, it's not. No nobility in that, just the way I am hard-wired.

When I write, I have other goals besides the literal exchange of writing for cash.

1. **Doing what I do well.** Which given my pretty much total absence of math, science, and technical skills is a good thing.
2. **Writing well is a challenge.** Bad writing is easy. But filling the blank page with words that grab a person by the heart and make them want to read is hard.
3. **People respond when I write.** When somebody says they read something I wrote it is like climbing a mountain and breathing in the sky. And when someone is actually moved by something I wrote? That's like finding a sack of diamonds at the top of that mountain, opening it up and being dazzled by the light.

Why am I writing?
I'm writing for hope.
Because after everything else —
Hope remains.

Renée and Yo

There was about to be a moment. One of those tiny moments one never forgets.

After spending some hours producing some unusually muddy writing, I was out for a head-clearing walk. Thinking about how I really didn't need the Popeye's Chicken calling me across the street from Lakeview High School. The neighborhood high school.

Suddenly cars pulled up and a woman popped out with a smile and such radiance, that even from fifty feet away, the most stubborn spring flowers would burst into bloom.

My eyes felt three times their normal size and all thoughts of Popeye's had fled. Next to emerge on the sidewalk was a slight, friendly-looking man in a blue shirt, sleeves rolled up. He looked like he could be some sort of Ambassador for World Harmony, somebody that everyone would want to know.

Lakeview High School is not some elite bastion of the super-rich. The late Tom Bosely, who played Richie Cunningham's father on "Happy Days," went to Lakeview. The movie "The Bodyguard" (not the one with Whitney Houston) was filmed at Lakeview, one of the best movies ever shot in the city. More than anything else, Lakeview is a neighborhood school. And these two magnetic people were not from the neighborhood. These two belonged to the world.

A small group surrounded the two as made their way inside. I suddenly recognized the man. "Hey! That's Yo Yo Ma!" What would he be doing here?

On my way home, the woman's identity came to me. That's Renée Fleming! To prove it to anyone who might question, I spent a good hour or so checking out pictures of Renée Fleming on the internet.

I also found that Fleming, Ma, and Damian Woetzel (former principal dancer with the New York City Ballet), were at Lakeview as part of a collaboration sponsored by the Chicago Symphony Orchestra, the Lyric Opera, and The Merit School of Music, simply intended to connect the arts to the way people live.

That's it. Nothing more. It wasn't sponsored by VISA. No political favors were exchanged. Instead, these world-class artists spoke with students, performed, and in their turn, they listened. The Poetry Club got up to recite as Yo Yo Ma played Bach. Fleming sang with the choir. Students looked on in amazement that a human being could really sing like that.

For a moment, the auditorium (normally filled with leaping and fidgeting teenagers) went totally still. Students turned off all their phones. Yo Yo Ma was playing Rachmaninoff.

For those students enrolled in performing arts classes, there was an awareness of a chance to go downtown to see some sort of performance. But on this day, these world-renowned artists had come to them.

In addition to their trip to Lakeview, Fleming and Ma gave an impromptu concert in the atrium of a downtown office building the next day. Bringing art to the people.

Meanwhile, back in the neighborhoods, heads were still reeling from the visit. More than one young boy or girl had the same thought. They were thinking, "Someday. Someday, I'm gonna do that too. Someday, when I am an artist and the world knows my name, I'm gonna remember what happened at my school when Renée Fleming and Yo Yo Ma dropped by. And I'll go back and visit with some kids."

Just like Renée Fleming and Yo Yo Ma.

Dirty People

It's a warm, windy Sunday afternoon in March at the Chicago Avenue bus stop. Keisha wrestles an overstuffed laundry bag almost as big as she is and waits fifteen to twenty minutes, service being reduced on the weekend. It's her only free day to make the three-quarter-mile trip west across the Chicago River, past the giant printing plant, and on to the nearest laundromat. This is a regular trip for her. She's smiling; she's got music, and the neighbor is looking after her two babies at home. Someone to watch her kids, because a little bit of the Cabrini Green community still exists in the row houses that make up the original Cabrini Green. Before they stacked people up in towers in the sky, they put them in row houses. Keisha knows she's lucky to have one to call home. The three-year waiting list was nothing for her.

When the tsunami-like wave of money rolled in from the east and north, gobbling up likely valuable land; the Cabrini Green towers started to buckle. People began to realize that stacking human beings in cinderblock cages on top of each other might not be such a great idea. When someone asked, "Where will the people from the community go, when there is no more community?" No one had an answer.

The Ten-Year Transformation Plan was a maze of good intentions, developer models, details confusing enough to require discussion long into the night, and a sprinkle of community input, all wrapped in the fog of bureaucratic indifference. No one seemed to have an answer to such questions as, "When this person from the seventeenth floor of Cabrini's Red Zone is forced to leave, what is the exact address where they will live?"

Which is why Keisha considers herself lucky. She has a place.

When developers came to rehab the original row houses, cost considerations (public housing, after all) meant setting priorities. Individual unit laundry hook-ups were eliminated. The story went that the sewer system couldn't handle public housing residents using their own washers and dryers, meaning the only reliable way to do laundry was to take a bus ride to the nearest laundromat.

Still, Keisha considers herself lucky. She takes a full load of med-tech courses downtown, works thirty hours a week at Potbelly Sandwiches, has her babies, and has all night for doing her schoolwork, so it isn't so bad. A weekly trip to the laundromat never hurt anyone, and it provides exercise.

When the Chicago Avenue bus pulls over, Keisha and her human sized laundry bag get on and take a seat near the front. The bus is crowded.

One stop later, the bus pulls over next to the giant 600 West Chicago building. Megan Pauly and Kristi

Pierce, barely glancing up from their phones long enough to stick their fare cards in the slot, take the only available seat, right behind Keisha.

Looking up, the two almost-interchangeable young blonde women slowly take in the fact that a giant laundry bag containing a week's worth of dirty clothes occupies the seat in front of them. They look at the bag, and one of them giggles. They both roll their eyes, and the other one says, "What. Ever."

Keisha hears the giggle, feels some sort of disturbance behind her. Doesn't know what it is and is too polite to turn and stare, much less say anything to the interchangeable women. She starts to get that warm, tired feeling she gets sometimes, like when her manager yells at the sandwich shop, then brushes behind her on the line way too close, or when it's one o'clock in the morning and she's still got another hour of homework to finish, or when one of her babies starts coughing and there is nothing, nothing, nothing she can do except to hold her tight and pray. That feeling.

And she remembers an old Tracy Chapman song, one her own mama used to sing to her, the part where she sings about being someone.

She remembers stories her grandma would tell her about how, back in the day, the Rev. Jesse Jackson would get folks to shout to the heavens all together when he sang out, "I AM! SOMEONE!" From the churches to the streets and everyplace in between. From every street corner in Chicago, "I AM SOMEONE!"

Keisha clutches her laundry bag and closes her eyes. From the seat right behind her, she hears one of the girls whisper to the other, *"Dirty people."*

Keisha feels the sickly hidden power of the words.

And fights to stay awake and ready.

Dear Keith Jarrett

The hardest part was keeping the secret that you were here, getting past the jaw dropping, bug-eyed desire to tell everyone I have ever known and ever will know, that my wife and I just met, talked with, and smiled a lot with Keith Jarrett while he ... um ... played the piano. Yep, we hung out with Keith Jarrett. More than once!

Respecting your privacy, we refrained from telling anyone that you were a regular just before the dinner hour at the Retirement Community where my mom lives. Sitting at the piano in the late afternoon light, right off the Dining Room, in the Community Family Room that feels like home, residents, friends, and families milled about (pre-Covid quarantine era). Some had no clue they were in the presence of a world renowned artistic original, a true giant in music history. Some did know who you were, like my wife, my siblings, and our mom. Some knew they were in the presence of greatness.

You were approachable and kind to all who stopped to chat or just to listen. When I asked my mom what you and she talked about, she answered, "Improvisation and Bach." And I could only repeat, "You talked about improvisation and Bach ... with Keith Jarrett ..." When you and I spoke, I said although my collection was respectable, I didn't have all of your ninety-two records. We talked about some of our favorites, then I stepped back to listen.

You started into a standard, laying down a chord the way Monet laid down a painting. I was taken back to the last time we saw your trio on a rainy September night inside Chicago's Symphony Center. As you told the story in the song, I saw myself standing on a cliff, about to jump, no clue what came next, only that I must jump. So, I did, flying and falling through open air, then somehow righting myself, slowed by the sound of your music, landing safe with the song. Your music had built a bridge across the wild, scary emptiness.

When I landed safe upon your musical bridge, I could once again hear the sound of hope.

Annie Beth Morningstar

She was the baby from the train that fell from the sky.

Did we catch her when she fell? I don't know. Maybe you should decide.

There were three of us. You, me, and the child. We named her Annie Beth Morningstar. We couldn't give her much, but we gave her that name.

And I still wonder, even after all these years, why us?

Why were we the ones who caught the baby who fell from the train that fell from the sky?

The story started in the deepest winter.

First, You

Across the years, I am calling you back to remember that first night. In the smoky dark club overlooking the baseball stadium, winter howled outside the second-floor picture window, and you stood at the bar with a group, drawing the stares of any breathing male.

I was never one to just stare, even if I had to wait in line. I made my way through the crowd and simply stood in front of you. Your eyes narrowed, registering the mystery of that bold move, while I said, "You are so far out of my league, it would be an honor just for you to tell me to get lost."

Something shifted out of range, those dancing winter winds taking the lead. I saw the smile you thought you were hiding, and with widened eyes you stared hard enough to see my future. You said, "Anybody with a line that cheesy needs work." Your laugh was like a river running straight from your soul. "How can I tell you to get lost? You obviously need a lot of help." We both laughed, and like an unspoken promise, everything changed.

The late-night rhythm struck a new beat. We started talking, the crowds thickened, and we slid into a kind of dance. There was a moment when your back was up against a scratchy brick wall, with your arms around my neck, and you said, "I don't do stuff like this." That kiss made us both forget our names. That moment erased everyone in that smoky loud room but you and me.

Then, The Accident

A week later came the accident that choked the whole city with pain. The accident and the baby on the train.

They're called 'El' trains, elevated maybe two stories above the street on rusty iron superstructures that break apart every ray of sun brave enough to shine. Circling a loop of downtown Chicago, they rumble through the sky. Any human being in downtown Chicago who has looked up at the El has, at some point in their lives, asked themselves what would happen if one of those screeching steel monsters fell off the track. But no, that could never really happen. Until it did.

At 5:23 on a rainy gray winter evening, the streets were jammed with rivers of people and vehicles. A motorman on the El paused at just the wrong moment – maybe there was a little bit of something he smoked, maybe not – and one car slammed into the back of another train. Two train cars jackknifed into the air, in slow motion, the wheels peeled from their tracks. Screams, stopped hearts, and terror blanketed souls like sweat. Glass shattered, metal twisted, bodies flew as two cars full of people tumbled over the side of the track and smashed onto the street forty feet below. One car was left hanging, jammed with terrified commuters, dangling in horror. Pointing straight down, maybe ten or twelve feet from the hard, cold street, the train car swung in the winter wind.

Ambulances lined up, engines humming, red lights strobing across the steel supports where the one train car still dangled, hanging from the sky.

Eleven people died hard deaths. The screams of the one hundred and eighty injured filled the night, crushing the heart of the city.

The hospitals ran out of beds, so they started putting people on the psych wards. Had to. No other choice. On the adolescent psych ward where I worked as a counselor, we set up cots in the day room and took in five victims. Five shattered souls who would never forget the terror of their train leaving the track and roaring out into the open air.

With no empty beds, there was no one else to claim the baby, so we took her on the psych ward. Like the first responders at the scene, those of us on the ward had no idea how the baby survived the crash. It was as if this baby could fly.

The Flying Baby

The Head Nurse, Larissa, had seen everything the street had to dish out. This was a woman who knew what the word triage meant ... even she was stopped cold by the flying baby.

Since we had no cribs, we pushed two armchairs together in the nurse's station. Aunt Sally, as we called one of our older nurses, shook her head, looked down on the child, and exclaimed, "Our own lil' baby Jesus!" To which Larissa replied, "If that's who this child is, then it turns out that Baby Jesus is a girl, Sally."

The tiny stranger, looking up at the circle of heads surrounding her, didn't seem the least bit scared. A little bruised, breathing calmly, she appeared to be eighteen, maybe nineteen months old. All of us had heard the first thing the EMT had said when he wheeled her into our ward. "But I tell you people, I did not know that babies could fly."

The EMT continued, "She was in one of the cars that flew off the track and bounced off the ground. I found her in a pool of broken glass on the sidewalk. Smiling and gurgling. Not a single cut from all that glass. Barely a bump from the fall. More like she had just woken up from a nap. Nobody around her survived. No one. Just this one little child. As if she could fly. I swear. It was just like she could fly, slide on, and land sweetly gently on the street, waiting calmly for what comes next."

Annie Beth Morningstar

Later that night, I called you to say I was working a double shift and wouldn't be home until morning. I told you the story of the baby, and you asked me her name. I said no one knew, and that's when you came up with Annie Beth Morningstar. You didn't think about it. You said it right away. As if there was no other choice. You gave her that name. So that's who she became.

The next morning, we had breakfast at Nookie's. Over the eggs and sausage and coffee, we decided that you would come with me at the start of my afternoon. shift, and visit little Annie.

Later that morning, we walked back to your place for love and the only rest we could find.

When you came with me to my shift later that afternoon, we found that little Annie had been moved to the Prentice Women's hospital on the other side of the building. You got to see her, though. I'll never forget your face when you first saw her; you looked ready to sit down and start making plans with her.

It took almost two weeks to find the parents. They had both been seriously injured, the father was in a coma, and the mother had suffered a head injury, causing some memory loss. For those weeks, no one came forward to gather up and hold onto that little baby miracle, so, we would see her. We would see Annie every day. The nurses always let us in so we'd sit with her, sing to her, rock her to sleep. Sometimes she'd smile and look at us as if we all shared a secret. Catching her with smiles as she drifted off to sleep.

For a while she was just ours.

Up until that day her parents arrived.

I remember handing Annie Beth over to a woman I must suppose was her mother. Annie's eyes were troubled. She gurgled and cried as she flailed, found your finger, and held on tight. She squeezed your finger, beaming you a smile, a smile that would have to do. Beyond her, the hospital room door opened, as if a train were about to board for a trip to some other distant sky.

After Annie

How do you lose something that was never really yours?

That winter, Annie's winter, sputtered into a lifeless spring. Every corner of Chicago was painted its own shade of grey.

One grey spring morning, soon after losing Annie, we woke up at the exact same time, looked at each other, and both said, "Road Trip."

How easy it was, back then, to just jump out of bed, slide into the car or hop over to the airport, and just get out of town. Packing was a 90-second prospect. No vitamins, medicines, lotions or potions, no preparation for weather changes. No reservations or planning the route. It was just "Go!" And if we got lost, we would just drive until we weren't lost anymore.

Maybe our road trip was a buried cry to losing Annie. Or maybe not. We weren't all that deep-thinking then. If some great cosmic voice from the sky spoke to us, "Do you realize this will be your last trip together?" we probably would have just turned to each other and asked, "Did you hear something?" pause a beat to laugh, and then say in unison, "Nah."

Somehow, we knew we were driving south. How we got to North Carolina is a mystery, but we arrived at the Outer Banks. Camping amid the salty smells and sounds of the ocean, we drifted off to sleep. That's when the rain started. Before long, it got seriously torrential to the point of scary. The tent collapsed, and we gathered up everything. Tripping and slipping and giggling in the in the mud, soaked to the skin, we ran for the car, tossed our stuff into the back seat, and started driving through the wet Carolina night. With only the rain and the empty, middle-of-the-night road, we headed for your parents' roof three hours away, or maybe not.

For a while, we were quiet, listening to the rhythm of the wipers, and breathing in scents of the green forest rain. Turning away from me, your eyes searched among the darkness of the pine trees. Turning back to me, your eyes wide and bright as starlight after rain, you said, "Think she'll remember us?"

I looked at you and said, "She will."

And you answered, "We can hope."

Houseless

She lays a yellow daffodil on the blue plastic
dashboard of the old green Honda.

Pillows, blankets, towels in the back seat.
What's left of their clothes in the trunk.

"See?" she says.
"Just like home."
Not homeless. Just houseless.
And it just can't be like this forever.
Hardest is finding a place to clean up.
Brushing teeth in gas station sinks.

It's noon on a Friday.
Darkened sky as if there never was a sun.
They move with the traffic.
The few who still have jobs heading home for an
early weekend.
The two in the Honda — not homeless — they are
houseless — find the flow and drive.

When this all started, they were worried most 'bout
the privacy
but no one really sees them.
And there are no phones.
It's not so bad.

And it just can't be like this forever.

By nightfall, they're so tired, it's easy to sleep
anywhere.
Hard part is one has to stay awake to wait for
the glass to smash, the steel cylinder, the oily smell
of gun.

They have to save the car.
Because they know about the shelters.
And after that comes only cardboard.
Their blanket can't look too good, or it's gone too.

Car as home came so fast.
From living in the house to living in the car was
such a thin cold line
the TV set, big winter coats, and shoes.

When he got sick, they closed the store, lost their
insurance, became invisible.
One day they were serving food to the homeless at
the Wednesday night meal.

And then a light went out. Some problems with the
insurance.
Now they're the ones lining up to eat.

   And it just can't be like this forever.

Come three o'clock on that dark afternoon,
Everybody almost home now.
Everybody almost home,
but the couple in the Honda

They keep driving, in the crowded car called home.

"See, she says, we still got some music."
On the radio, Sam Cooke sings about changes.

"I can drive for awhile," she says.

"You just rest. Close your eyes."

And it just can't be this way forever.

Thanksgiving Alone

I could do Thanksgiving alone. Lots of people do that.

Hanging up the phone, I barely remembered why she cancelled, something about "needing space." I was too busy preparing to be a frozen turkey dinner tough guy. Recalling, from experience, that shirttails don't offer protection for pulling a hot pan from the oven.

There was really no one to call. It was Wednesday. Thanksgiving was tomorrow. Expecting an out-of-town guest, I had already begged off all invitations from my two aunts. And it wasn't like I had a phone book full of friends to call. Or even a scrap from the corner of a phone book page.

Back when people used phone books. It was different then, Chicago was a grid of streets and alleys colored only in history and shades of gray, especially in the slippery shadow winds of November. Now, rainbow flowers spill out of traffic medians, and thousands upon thousands of newly-planted trees have flourished.

Then, in the late 1970's, Chicago had emerged from its years as a brooding black, railroad crossroad muscle of manufacturing soot, and the air had lightened to gray. There was a woman mayor, a tough Irish lady named Jane Byrne who had electrified the city by actually winning. Instead of stacking the souls of poor people straight up into the sky in housing projects, she was going to spend a week living in Cabrini Green, a housing project just over the line that marked where I felt safe to walk. I didn't know what I thought about her moving in to Cabrini Green for a week, but I knew it was different.

That was a time when I sensed something was just about to happen in Chicago.

On that late Wednesday afternoon before Thanksgiving, the city felt deserted. It felt as if all the people had somehow been sucked into airplanes (like the one she would not be on) and blown out to grandmothers' houses over a million different rivers and woods.

The best way to make sure I was ready for my Thanksgiving alone was to go for a walk. Having come from a family of walkers, I pretty much believed that going for walk was the way to get ready for anything.

In the early grey glow of twilight, I set out into the empty streets and sidewalks, rounding first the school where I was a special education teacher. It had only been a few hours since we had closed up the education shop early. But people need touchstones when they walk, and back then, the school was mine. It was one of the beating hearts of a neighborhood called Uptown.

In his classic book *Working*, Chicago legend Studs Terkel wrote about the school.

There were also streets in that neighborhood that were best not walked by at all. I had learned those streets by following along with the guy who had hired me to be a teacher. His name was Pat. He started what was then called a Free School in the late sixties, As the neighborhood and the needs changed over the years, it became a special education school. The thing I loved about a classroom of twenty-five kids, teaching all subjects, was that in special ed, the kid came first, then the subject. If a kid started bouncing a basketball in the middle of social studies, I coaxed the dribbler into a game of catch and then, with the ball flying back and forth, I could lead us all back to social studies. I didn't worry so much about rules.

Most important was that school didn't end at the walls of the classroom. Sometimes when kids didn't or couldn't show up in the morning, I'd follow Pat east on Montrose Avenue, turn left at Beacon, run to the back of a building while Pat started ringing doorbells. And when the kids came rushing out the back door, I'd corral them, and we'd all trudge back to the school.

But on that afternoon before Thanksgiving, as I walked east on Montrose, crossed Clark Street, and looked north into those very same streets, even they seemed somehow deserted. A lonely tumbleweed could go blowing right through. There was no sign of any of my kids.

Since it wasn't dark yet, I wasn't yet ready to hole up alone for the holiday in my little yellow kitchen with the round table, so I kept walking towards the lake. When all else fails, keep walking towards the water.

Walking alone would be good practice for being alone. I was still glad I hadn't attached myself to some gathering or another. The only thing worse than being alone was being alone in a crowd.

But I could do Thanksgiving alone. Lots of people do that. I had plenty of beer to drink, football games to watch, and food I didn't know how to cook. I had frozen dinners that were no problem to heat up. (This was back in the time when a person could hum songs with lyrics about books and poetry and those were brand new thoughts.)

Still walking, almost to the Lake, I turned right on inner Lake Shore Drive, and that's when I saw him.

As the last of that grey light was just about to fall, I saw the bright red and white checked shirt, like a walking beacon of hope, underneath the open gray raincoat. Walking alone. Just like me.

It was Studs Terkel. Of course, I knew who it was. Every single person in Chicago would know who it was. I had grown up in a house where Studs Terkel was always on the radio. I had to say something to him. We were the only people on the street. I had to say something and I did have a connection. I really was a teacher at a school that he wrote about in his book. So, I took a deep breath.

"Good afternoon or evening, Mr. Terkel."

"Well good afternoon, young fella. What brings you out on these streets today?"

"Oh, just walking." I told him my name and said, "I'm a teacher. I work at the Southern School. Pat hired me. I saw when you came in once for a Board Meeting, but we never met."

"Ah a teacher!" he spoke in the deep warm gravel of a voice I had only heard on the radio. Smiling, he said, "If Pat hired you, you must also be a good teacher. Pat's in my book *Working* you know."

"Yes sir. I know. My copy of the book is very well read. And thank you sir. I guess I'm learning as I go. School is over for the holiday now. It's kind of empty out here."

"Ah," said Studs Terkel. "Empty? No. Keep listening. It's not empty at all. Especially for a young teacher. You just keep listening young man. You just keep listening."

The exchange took five seconds. It happened a long time ago. Even after all these years, I remember how good that frozen turkey dinner tasted, and how, not for one moment that Thanksgiving did I feel alone.

Chicago Paris Dream

In the tired grey morning rain, I board the El train in Chicago, reach up to grab the strap, and stand shoulder to shoulder on the crowded train. She shoots a fast glance as the train lurches forward and our shoulders touch. Decides I'm safe, leans down to keep scrolling her phone, and shakes the red hair from her face. The train slows, a seat opens, so I invite her to sit down with my eyes and a nod of my head. She does. From the packed aisle of the train, no one moves to sit next to her. She looks up at me and with a tiny smile of amusement and a shake of the head that asks the world, "Was it something I said?"

So, I sit down next to her. Shoulder to shoulder. Thighs lightly grazing as the train rumbles and clanks to the center of the city. She looks up from her phone with a hint, then the memory, of a smile. Perhaps, as we touch shoulders, she sees me and wonders about a grandfather she never knew.

When the train doors swish open, I hear the rain.

***

And with the rain, I am back in Paris. Water washing down the gutters of the ancient stone streets, down paths that flow, like time, from the gleaming white Basilica Sacre Coeur. I smell coffee that lights up the morning.

I am, once again, six hours or so from sitting down next to you for the very first time on the steps of that high Basilica, gazing out together over Paris in the midday sunlight, and saying the absolute most profound thing I could come up with at the time, which was, "Wow."

At which point, you look over with only enough interest to smirk, "That was deep."

A few seconds pass, you get up, pause for one more look at the rippling city in the sunlight below, and stretch.

Knowing I had to say something to keep you from walking away, I mumble something about being hungry. Probably something dumb like, "Know where you can get any good French food around here?" Then (and this is a mystery I never have and never will — until my very last breath — figure out), we are in a café. There is wine that amazes, cheese and fruit and sausage, and the shadows fall in a way that marks time moving at the speed of light.

We never stop talking.

My new book has just come out. I begin reading you stories out loud. I tell you how the blonde came back with coffee and croissants one spring morning and announced, "Roger? I'm a Princess. I just thought you should know."

The Princess was soon gone. Vanished except for the way she hovered over so many stories. And now you're gone too.

Which is why it's so strange that you keep coming back and filling in what's between the lines of all these new stories. Between the lines, where important parts of the story go unsaid, except for their reverberations. Like the way that folk singer's voice reverberates in that smoky bar on the tiniest of alleys winding downhill from the Basilica — the way her voice is somehow shaky and strong at the very same time. Singing that song about how the timing was wrong.

You like your music to howl, to cry, to sing to distant stars. No wimpy ass folk music for you, you don't even like Dylan. We are saved when we both settle in and stay firm on John Hiatt. That night the folk singer does her set, sings her song about timing being wrong, I guess it does nothing for you. I guess quietly because I don't really want to know the answer. I just want you and Paris. I want you both like you are some giant bowl of buttered, salted popcorn, and if I just keep eating, keep stuffing that salty, buttered taste of fluffy popcorn in my mouth, then some day you will roll down your drawbridge, reveal the solid, whip-smart, grounded, laughing haven of your generous soul, loving me clear-eyed at least as much as I love you. Because we have plans and golden promises.

You ask for my plans and I start babbling about the next book. We walk back to sit on the steps of the Basilica to look out over Paris bathed in the timeless night magic of the lights. And I babble.

I tell you the title, *Street Corner Spirits*. The stories will be mysteries, all of which seemed to start inside the doors of that Basilica. Though I see mysteries inside those doors, you see rules. Still, you see that next book better than anyone.

But when our eyes are reflected in the stars that sing together with the lights of the city, I think if I love someone enough, eventually they will change.

And of course, that doesn't happen.

So, the city lights dim. And you stay, until it is time for both of us to go.

As much as I sing and write about all those mysteries you never believe in, what I cannot imagine, even in the parts between the lines, is that a return is possible. I cannot imagine you would come back. But you do come back.

You come back right this very moment.

***

The Chicago train swishes into the Grand Station, she rises from our shared seat, and wonder of wonders, leaves a smile for her imagined grandfather, me. She smiles at me and there you are. In her smile I see you.

Right here in this story, the young woman leaves the train, and you come back. You come back like a memory of hope. A Paris Dream. Woven into a Chicago rain ride.

And that will have to do.

Last Word in Hope's Garden

The cicadas play their symphony to mark the fading summer. Though I have passed his garden in the daytime, this twilight view is one I've never seen before. A waist high jungle of billowing green topped by generous white hydrangea flowers stretches over the corner between sidewalk and street. Spanning two sides of the red brick building, orderly pots are interspersed with playful mischief of smiling gnomes, a ceramic squirrel, some tiny chairs and a table perfect for giggling fairy-dust visitors.

The next time I walk by, I see him out working. I express my admiration for the way he took this one city corner and made it magical, took the space and made it beautiful.

He shrugs and says "Thank you," in the Swiss German accent that speaks of other times, other Labor Days, other working people living their lives here near this corner on the northwest side of Chicago. His shoulders rise again as he takes in the corner with a sweep of this hand, "It keeps me working. Keeps me busy."

He reaches down to pull a stray weed and, as he rises, a brilliant green swarm of wild parakeets flutters into the trees that blanket the Corner Garden. The old man looks up at the newly arrived guests, smiles and says, "Ah, here they are again. Watching over the work."

"They bring me hope."

Acknowledgements

To the great Chicago writers who inspire me: Bill Brashler, Studs Terkel, Mike Royko, Bill Granger, James T. Farrell, and Nelson Algren.

To <u>everyone</u> connected to the gone-but-not-forgotten sites, Open Salon and Fictionique, where several of these stories made their first appearance.

To Diana Ani Stokely, whose partnership made this book a reality. To Amy McVay Abbott for her insight and encouragement.

And finally, to Maria: Once again the heart and soul.

About the Author

Roger Wright has been writing since he could hold a pencil. Along the way he has been a bartender, truck driver, bookstore clerk, ghost writer, Special Education teacher, counselor, and training and leadership development consultant for businesses, faith-based organizations, government, and non-profit groups.

Wright is the author of *Finding Work When There Are No Jobs* and co-author of *I Am Your Neighbor: Voices from a Chicago Food Pantry.*

Made in the USA
Monee, IL
06 January 2022

87032747R00105